# Kill
# and
# Overkill

*The Strategy of Annihilation*

*Books by Ralph E. Lapp*

Man and Space: The Next Decade

Roads to Discovery

The Voyage of the Lucky Dragon

Radiation: What It Is and How It Affects You
    (*with Jack Schubert*)

Atoms and People

The New Force

Nuclear Radiation Physics
    (*with H. L. Andrews*)

Must We Hide?

Kill and Overkill

# Kill
# and
# Overkill

## *The Strategy of Annihilation*

RALPH E. LAPP

Basic Books, Inc., New York

Publishers

*Second printing*

© *1962 by Ralph E. Lapp*
*Library of Congress Catalog Card Number: 62–17243*
*Printed in the United States of America*
*Designed by Laurel Wagner*

To

who, more than any other scientist,
has pioneered in the understanding
of the atomic revolution.

# Contents

| | | |
|---|---|---|
| 1 | *The President's Decision* | 3 |
| 2 | *The Tragedy of Science* | 15 |
| 3 | *The Family of Bombs* | 23 |
| 4 | *The Incredible Stockpile* | 39 |
| 5 | *Blast, Fire, and Fallout* | 49 |
| 6 | *The Missiles* | 65 |
| 7 | *The Paradoxes of Deterrence* | 79 |
| 8 | *The Game of Nuclear War* | 93 |
| 9 | *Is Defense Possible?* | 109 |
| 10 | *Accident, Miscalculation, or Madness* | 123 |
| 11 | *"The Hope of Civilization"* | 137 |
| NOTES AND REFERENCES | | 155 |
| INDEX | | 189 |

"Oh, where are you coming from, soldier, gaunt soldier
With weapons beyond any reach of my mind,
With weapons so deadly the world must grow older
And die in its tracks, if it does not turn kind?"

STEPHEN VINCENT BENET, *Song for Three Soldiers*

# Kill
# and
# Overkill

*The Strategy of Annihilation*

# 1

# *The President's Decision*

*"Every man, woman, and child lives under a nuclear sword of Damocles, hanging by the slenderest of threads, capable of being cut at any moment by accident, miscalculation, or madness."*

These were the anxious words with which President John F. Kennedy addressed the United Nations on September 25, 1961, eight months after he had taken office. No doubt he had been aware in advance of the heavy responsibilities he was undertaking as President. But it is doubtful that he, or any person becoming head of a nuclear power, could appreciate the full horror of his position until he came face to face with his burden as Commander-in-Chief. For the finger

3

that might push the button unleashing the fury of nuclear war was now his.

It is true that under the Constitution only Congress may declare war. But this proviso has become a kind of vermiform appendix. Our founding fathers, living in the era of the rifle, the knife, and the bow and arrow, did not foresee the day of intercontinental missiles loaded with nation-destroying warheads. In the nuclear age, Congress itself has delegated to the President the responsibility of pushing the button.

In the mid-1960s a United States President must live constantly with the threat of missile war and the hideous possibility of the ultimate decision. The fabled sword of Damocles threatened only Damocles; the nuclear sword threatens all mankind. Within our decade the United States, and presumably the Soviet Union, will possess thousands of intercontinental ballistic missiles, ready to fire at the touch of a button. Both nations will be on endless alert, prepared to hurl salvos of ICBMs at each other—a process to which the military refers delicately as "mutual terror through strategic exchange." Unless there is a drastic relaxation of the Cold War and a change in the basic condition of man, the maintenance of peace will hang only on the capacity for mutual annihilation.

How insecure that reliance is can be made vividly clear if we look at the war-triggering process. We do not know how the machinery is set up in the Soviet Union, but presumably it is not very different from our own defense-and-retaliation system.

The United States President is never more than seconds away from contact with the firing centers. Direct communication with the lookout and command posts travels with him wherever he goes—in his airplane, in his automobile, at his conferences, on the golf course, everywhere. The alarm, if and when it is sounded, will come from Norad (North American Air Defense Command), which continually receives and analyzes information from the continental network of radars scanning the skies day and night. To take instant action, the President has direct lines to the Strategic Air Command (SAC) and the command center for the roving Polaris submarines. And his decision, to act or not to act, will have to be made within 15 minutes or less, for that is all the warning time a missile attack will allow.

It is not unreasonable to hypothesize a situation like the following:

> SCENE: The Presidential yacht, which is cruising up the Potomac in the early morning hours with the sleeping Presidential party. Time: 3 A.M. The President is returning to Washington from Norfolk, where he christened the first of a new class of submarines the day before. The sky is overcast, the weather sultry and warm even for late August. The President is in deep, exhausted sleep, after having stayed up late discussing a disturbing midnight news broadcast with his aides.
>
> At 3:02 a coded message, preceded by a special symbol, is received in the radio room. The startled officer in charge knows the urgency of the symbol and decodes the message at once. It is from Norad: CONDITION RED—REPEAT, CONDITION RED—BMEWS HAS PICKED UP SEVERAL HUNDRED OBJECTS OVER THE NORTH POLE—COMPUTERS PREDICT IMPACT ON USA IN TWELVE MINUTES—ICBM IDENTIFICATION PROBABLE —SAC ALERTED—CD SIGNAL HOLDING.
>
> The officer races to the President's bedroom. Inside, the loud alarm of the SAC red telephone already is ringing furiously, but it has not yet penetrated the President's sleep. The guards at the door, fumbling with their keys in the excitement, finally get the door unlocked and the President is awakened.

5

The Norad message is specific enough, but to the half-aroused President it still seems a dream. He has been dreaming about the new submarine he christened and its three-megaton missiles, and also about the disquieting midnight newscast: that the Chinese had successfully tested their first H-bomb in the Sinkiang area.

It is no time for dreaming. The President, now agonizingly awake, reads the Norad message again. It makes no sense. Nothing in the events of recent days has suggested that a crisis or attack was imminent.

But the minutes are flying, and the "several hundred objects," if they are indeed missiles, will soon be falling upon American bases or cities or both.

For a moment, the agony of decision is put off. The President demands more positive information from BMEWS (the Ballistic Missile Early Warning System) and Norad. An order goes to the Andrews Air Force Base outside Washington to ready a SAC jet plane for take-off; the President will fly in the plane as his emergency base of command. A helicopter is dispatched from the Quantico Marine Base to rendezvous with the yacht and speed the President to Andrews.

Now, while he waits for the helicopter, the President can no longer evade the big decision. Shall he give the signal to strike the presumed attacker with the full, fantastic power of SAC and the missile arsenal? No man in history has ever weighed a decision so fateful for humanity.

A flash from Norad: HOLD—HOLD—OBJECTS IDENTIFIED AS METEORS—NO ATTACK—REPEAT, RADAR OBJECTS ARE METEORS, NOT MISSILES.


So narrow is the margin between mankind and disaster. Fortunately our example here is hypothetical, and we can give it a happy ending. But it is all too close to what might occur, and in fact to incidents that have actually occurred. In an alarm of this kind, the nation would sleep on, unaware of the crisis on the Potomac and of how narrowly it had escaped the pushing of the button.

In a very real sense the public is sleeping, so far as the grave issues of nuclear war are concerned. The American people, and the peoples of other nations, have only a hazy conception of the grotesque proportions to which nuclear weapons have grown and of the size of the bomb stockpile. And when they think about the problem of nuclear war at all, they dismiss it as too terrible to be a real possibility. The United States and the Soviet Union are pictured as two adversaries standing face to face with loaded pistols, but with the triggers wired together. Only a madman, people reason, would pull the trigger.

At the same time, paradoxically, the nuclear powers act as if their only hope for security lay in building bigger and bigger arsenals. President Kennedy, explaining his decision to resume nuclear tests in 1962, stated:

> "But until mankind has abolished both war and its instruments of destruction, the United States must maintain an effective quantity and quality of nuclear weapons, so deployed and protected as to be capable of surviving any surprise attack and devastating the attacker. Only through such strength can we be certain of deterring a nuclear strike, or an overwhelming ground attack, upon our forces and allies. Only through such strength can we in the free world—should that deterrent fail—face the tragedy of another war with any hope of survival."

Our military leaders appear to believe that nuclear war would not be the end of everything—that such a war could be "won." But even they lack full conviction, for so thoroughly military a thinker as General Douglas MacArthur has come to the opposite view. He said in 1961:

> "Global war has become a Frankenstein to destroy both sides. No longer is it a weapon of adventure—the short cut to

7

international power. If you lose, you are annihilated. If you win, you stand only to lose. No longer does it possess even the chance of the winner of a duel. It contains now only the germs of double suicide."

How, indeed, would a nation measure a "win"? What arithmetic or statistics could determine whether a nation had gained its war aim? Would the death of 50 per cent of its population and the destruction of its national life represent survival? Would annihilation of the enemy nation be victory?

The feelings of most civilians are probably like those expressed in the ironic words of the writer James R. Newman:

> "Leaders of opinion declare that a nuclear war is unthinkable. But we must be armed to the teeth and prepared to retaliate, bomb for bomb, two for one if possible. And yet in such a conflict the nation fighting to preserve itself cannot preserve itself, and all must perish."

A spirit of helpless bafflement, almost of despair, seems to have settled upon the people of the nations involved in the Cold War. They live in daily dread not only of man-created tensions but also of the frightening advance of technology. There is a growing apprehension that the ultimate decision will be taken not by man's own will but by his hardware. W. H. Pickering, the well-informed director of the Jet Propulsion Laboratory at the California Institute of Technology, has voiced such a thought:

> "This is the prospect we face: the decision to destroy an enemy nation—and by inference our own—will be made by a radar set, a telephone circuit, an electronic computer. It will be arrived at without aid of human intelligence. If a human observer cries: 'Stop, let me check the calculations,' he is al-

ready too late—his launching sites are destroyed and the war is lost.

"It is a frightening prospect. Far more than being slaves to our machines, our very lives depend upon the accuracy and reliability of a computing machine in a far distant country. The failure of a handful of vacuum tubes and transistors could determine the fate of our civilization."

Dr. Pickering explained that we are on the verge of an era of military automation in which every important city on our planet can be equated with a push-button somewhere which is prepared to launch an all-destroying missile against that city. Whether the missile is launched deliberately or by an electronic aberration, the city is doomed.

In this light, even the weapons of warfare are no longer a strictly military affair, to be handled solely in traditional military terms. The problems of nuclear warfare are not really military in nature, nor does military training *per se* endow anyone with special wisdom or competence in the waging of such war. What is particularly military about an ICBM that can be handled and checked only by a crew of physical technicians? Does it take a military officer to press a button? Is a General in any way especially qualified to evaluate the conduct of a war which will consist of massive exchanges of ICBMs and may be ended within an hour?

If the weapons themselves are no longer strictly soldiers' tools, in the traditional sense, nuclear *strategy* is even farther removed from the limited competence of the military mind. In pre-atomic times military strategy was based on time, space, and freedom to maneuver, and on amassing sufficient supplies of weapons. Generals and admirals felt that they could never have too many tanks, ships, planes, guns, and bombs. In the thermonuclear age conditions are

9

utterly different. The time scale of warfare has been reduced to minutes. Once the salvos of missiles begin, there can be no maneuvering of forces or defense of territory. And a build-up of an unlimited stockpile of nuclear weapons only tends to convince an enemy that he is in mortal danger and must strike first.

The strategic policies of the United States Defense Department over the past decade dramatically illustrate the results and the lack of imagination of the military approach. Although our defense system is under ultimate civilian control, it has been shaped largely by the military. There is every evidence that the dominating policy has been an unlimited build-up of arms—the hardware came first, the philosophy could come later. The military frantically pushed the development of ICBMs and located the major missile bases in the United States heartland, thus exposing the population and the nation's food-growing areas, along with the bases, to attack. The Air Force also accumulated an immense armada of 630 B-52 bombers, each capable of carrying nearly 50 megatons of H-bombs—a strategic striking force so powerful that it went far beyond the bounds of any rational objective. The nation's arsenal of weapons, in short, has grown to a monstrous stockpile which could not only kill, but overkill, any possible enemy or group of enemies. In the name of defense, the military has pursued a policy which an outside observer might well regard as a strategy of annihilation.

All this is hardly calculated to ameliorate the situation which J. Robert Oppenheimer described as "two scorpions in a bottle" and which President Dwight D. Eisenhower, addressing the United Nations in 1953, referred to as "two atomic colossi . . . doomed malevolently to eye each other indefinitely across a trembling world."

Quite plainly national defense, to paraphrase Clemenceau, has become too important to be left to the military. In the present state of the world, it would be foolhardy for the United States to disarm or even give the appearance of disarming, since even that would dismay its allies. But in the realm of arms, security would be best served by a stable deterrent, rather than an overwhelming force of limitless threat to all the world.

More fundamentally, it has become imperative that every citizen understand the true nature of the danger and the forces we must control. Man is engaged today in a struggle not only with himself but also with the technology he has created. Science has released a jinni which threatens to get entirely out of hand. The scientists cannot stuff it back into the bottle; we must instead learn to master it. As Eugene Rabinowitch, editor of the *Bulletin of the Atomic Scientists* and one of the most conscientious fighters for a return to nuclear sanity, has observed:

> "The world in which nuclear forces are on the loose is a world in which man cannot survive by the same kind of endurance, cleverness, and luck which have permitted him to survive in the 'chemical' world of yesterday. The rapid advance of scientific thought has projected mankind into an alien world. . . . Man can survive in this world of incredible violence only by a similarly spectacular progress in social and political wisdom."

We need to be mindful of the fantastic amount of human effort, in time, money, and thought, that is being swallowed up in the dangerous and futile aggrandizement of weapons of destruction—and is thereby being diverted from the essential quest of which Dr. Rabinowitch speaks. In weapons research and development alone (to say nothing of weapons production) the United States spent $80 billion in the 1950 decade. Who knows what constructive works of science and technology might have been achieved for the benefit of mankind if the arrow of our effort had been directed toward peaceful goals?

The atom and the rocket, twin revolutionary forces of our time, are not easy to understand. "These secret and complex things," the average citizen is apt to say, "are better left to the experts." But such an attitude, and the secrecy with which our Government insists on surrounding the whole area of weapons, are fatal enemies of democracy. If the American people are judged incapable of understanding the vital issues or not to be trusted with the vital information, then they are no longer the determiners of their future.

President Kennedy, in his message on national security to the Congress in 1961, offered some reassuring words on this subject:

> "Our arms must be subject to ultimate civilian control and command at all times, in war as well as peace. The basic decisions on our participation in any conflict and our response to any threat—including all decisions relating to the use of nuclear weapons or the escalation of a small war into a large one —will be made by the regularly constituted civilian authorities."

Regularly constituted civilian authorities, in the American system, represent the voters, and it is from the voters that they must get their ultimate instructions. The wisdom of their decisions will depend in the last analysis on the temper and wisdom of the public. Therein lies the best hope of mankind's survival. As Ernest Bevin told the House of Commons a few months after Hiroshima:

> "There has never been a war which, if the facts had been put calmly before the ordinary folk, could not have been pre-

vented. The common man is the greatest protection against war."

How did we get where we are? What are the facts, as opposed to the daily din of propaganda with which we are deluged, about the fateful weapons, the arms race, the strategies, and the questions and issues that occupy the minds of the inner circles in Washington and Moscow (and other capitals as well)? In the chapters that follow we shall try to explore these not-so-mysterious facts and questions.

# 2

# *The Tragedy of Science*

Animals do not make weapons; they defend their survival with fang and claw—with the natural instruments of their species. Man alone is distinguished by his purposeful invention of weapons for killing. He began by picking up rocks to hurl at his prey. Even these primitive missiles endowed him with formidable power, for they were coupled to a remarkable guidance and control system—his brain, a three-pound computer of wondrous design and capacity.

All too soon, man turned his weapons upon his own kind; the hunter became the hunted. Under the pressure of this competition, weaponry became a major human industry. Throughout the long warfare with his own species, a contest of offense and defense, man has worked toward ever more destructive weapons. The sword, the spear, the rifle, and the cannon each in its turn slew millions, but the brain of man has never paused in its search for more efficient instruments of slaughter.

In Bernard Shaw's *Man and Superman* the Devil observes sardonically, and not without truth, that man's "heart is in his weapons . . . in the arts of life man invents nothing, but in the arts of death he outdoes Nature herself . . . when he goes out to slay, he carries a marvel of mechanism that lets loose at the touch of his finger all the hidden molecular energies . . ."

In 1901, when Shaw wrote these words, the Devil had not yet let man in on the secret of *nuclear* energies. The crowning irony of mankind's war-darkened history is that this discovery—the most catastrophic contribution to the arts of death—came from the work of the gentlest and most pacifist of science's great geniuses, Albert Einstein. It was his now-famous formula $E=mc^2$, suggesting the immense energy lying in the core of the atom, that led to the A-bomb and the H-bomb.

To scientists, the tragedy of our age is that at the very time when science has reached a position where it can enormously improve man's life, its main thrust has been turned to destructive applications. This, of course, is not by the scientists' choice. They are merely the servants, most of them unwillingly, of the arms race generated by the Cold War, the terrifying new weapons, and the demands of national defense. The weapons and military technology are now so complex that they call for enlistment of the major part of a nation's scientific and engineering manpower. In fact, they have brought about a social revolution which is almost as disturbing as the revolution in warfare itself.

Never in history has a nation's brainpower been concentrated so massively on the problems of defense, in both its hot and cold aspects.

This state of affairs began in World War II, as a result of the vast new military technologies born of the war—not only the A-bomb but also radar, electronics, jet planes, rocketry, etc. Warfare was transferred to the laboratories, and the white-coated technician became a more important soldier than the gun-bearer in the field. Armies of specialists were assembled for each project. And many universities became almost branches of the military establishment.

Since the war, military research has spread even more widely into our national life. It is now supported by $10 billion per year from the Defense Department and involves government agencies, industry, and the universities. The military, imbued with an almost mystical faith in basic science as a result of the successes of the atomic physicists, has showered fat contracts upon university scientists. A generation ago most scientists would have scorned military work. But in 1960 one of our leading universities accepted more than $40 million of defense funds, 40 other universities received more than $1 million each, and there was hardly an institution of higher learning in the country which was not directly or indirectly a beneficiary of the Pentagon's interest in military science.

For the scientists, especially physicists, this has meant unprecedented affluence. Gone are the days when a physicist had to build his own instruments from odds and ends and beg a hundred dollars from the physics department fund to conduct a project. Even theoretical physicists, who used to work with no more equipment than a blackboard and a slide-rule, now have expensive electronic computers and preside over $100,000-a-year projects.

This subsidization of university scientists has had a doubly disturbing effect. On one hand, it has drawn many of the best minds into a preoccupation with weaponry which has made the scientist a sinister figure in the public mind; on the other, it has sadly undermined our universities as oases of pure learning.

Inevitably the academic scientist has been plunged into politics—as administrator of projects, as consultant on technical problems, and as adviser on policy and strategy. The marriage of science and politics has not been a happy one. After two decades of association, the scientists and politicians still do not speak each other's language or understand each other's point of view.

The politicians, though doubtful of the scientists' practical common sense, have developed a blind faith in science which is highly irritating to the men of science. Many seem to regard science as a kind of slot machine: just pump enough money into it and it will pay off. The physicist Hans Bethe, one of the scientists most frequently consulted by the Government, has protested: "Anybody who thinks that science can do anything, or fill any order you give it, obviously doesn't understand science." He added, with considerable understatement: "There is some vagueness and ignorance about science in some members of the Congress and in some committees of Congress. . . . It is also present in some lower echelons of the Defense Department."

The Congress must pass upon huge budgets for research and deal with many complex scientific issues. But there is not a single scientist among its membership. Many Congressmen have had too little formal education even to attempt to understand the riddles of science. Moreover, most of the men on Capitol Hill are so busy with daily appointments and political affairs that they have little time to learn anything new and difficult. In view of this, it is not easy to understand why the Congress has been so slow to equip itself with scientific advisers, as the President and his Executive departments have done. Very few committees on Capitol Hill have scientists on their working staffs. Even the Joint Committee on Atomic Energy, which watches over the nation's vast and complicated nuclear activities, lacks this kind of competence. True, it may consult the Atomic Energy Commission's scientists, but this hardly leaves it in a position to perform its supposed function as an independent "watchdog" over the AEC.

If the politicians are suspicious of scientists, the scientists, for their part, are baffled and bewildered by the politicians. In part this has been due to their own innocence and amateurism in politics. In the hurly-burly of politics, one must not be thin-skinned: "If you can't stand the heat, don't come into the kitchen." But the scientists' bafflement stems, in the main, from a deeper conflict. What has dismayed them most, and stunned many into timid silence, is the fact that, when called upon for advice on high policy, they have been denounced for giving honest opinions which the politicians find unacceptable.

The most publicized of these occasions was the famous debate in 1950 on whether to undertake the development of a hydrogen bomb. Many of the top-echelon scientific advisers, including J. Robert Oppenheimer and Hans Bethe, opposed the project. Bethe joined with others in taking the fight to the public, on the ground that it was a vital issue calling for democratic decision. Whether their advice on the issue was wrong is still debatable, for history has not yet shown what the ultimate results of the decision taken may be. But the real point of the affair is that the scientists' stand brought forth a political attack upon their patriotism. It was partly responsible for Oppenheimer's later expulsion from the Government's advisory councils. And while Oppenheimer was disgraced, Edward Teller, the chief champion of the H-bomb among the scientists, rose to high military favor and public prominence.

The hearings in the Oppenheimer case covered a great deal more ground than the case itself. Anyone who studies the voluminous transcript of those hearings will see there, set forth in the clearest terms, the dilemma of mankind—the conflict between conscience and the power drive. Many of the nation's leading scientists were called to testify, and they took the occasion to protest. Their plea, in essence, was for freedom to speak their minds, to have something to say about the purposes for which science was to be used. In strong terms they expressed their long-rankling distaste for being mere servants of the military and of power politics.

Let it be recalled that it was the scientists, those most directly involved in the creation of nuclear weapons, who were the first to propose and work for international disarmament and control of atomic energy. They have been almost alone in insisting upon public airing and wide, democratic discussion of the vital issues of H-bomb development, weapons testing, fallout, and the arms race. Most of them emphatically do not agree with Dr. Teller's view that the scientist's only job is to study "the laws of nature" and to "find the ways in which these laws can serve the human will," or that "it is *not* the scientist's job to determine whether a hydrogen bomb should be constructed or how it should be used." They feel that in matters of technical complexity, so poorly understood by laymen and government officials, they have a compelling duty of evaluation and education.

Yet the scientists are inextricably caught in the momentum of the arms race and are themselves helplessly contributing to its momentum. How could it be otherwise? A scientist working on seemingly abstract researches in his laboratory can have no foreknowledge about whether his findings may eventually be put to harmful use; Einstein and Lord Rutherford did not dream that their work in physics would one day lead to a Hiroshima. Nor can the scientists do anything to restrain the headlong onrush of technology. The late John von Neumann, a mathematical genius whose theoretical work sparked many technical developments, remarked that restraint of technology was impossible, because it was "contrary to the whole ethos of the industrial age." Not even the great destruction of World War II was sufficiently disillusioning to put a brake on technology; indeed, the war accelerated it.

Thus scientists and engineers cannot, either individually or collectively, control the course of technological events, even by quixotically taking a pledge not to work on any project that may result in disservice to mankind. About the only way a scientist can "go on strike" is to forsake his profession and become a baker or hairdresser.

Of course, our bright young men are not going into hairdressing. They have been growing up in a romantic era of ICBM toys in the nursery, of astronauts, and of home-made atom smashers. The most alluring careers, in terms of pay and excitement, are in science and technology. Meanwhile, the revulsion that afflicted scientists after Hiroshima is wearing off. Weapons-making has been splintered into intensely specialized jobs. Men work on gyromechanisms, on microminiaturized electronics, on plasma physics. It is easy to forget the monstrous machines of destruction to which their work is contributing.

The new generation has accepted its military employment as a natural condition. "Tens of thousands of scientists and technicians," notes the well-known scientist Harrison Brown, "have devoted all of their professional lives to the invention and construction of weapons. A majority of those who went to work after World War II are convinced that weaponry is a way of life for themselves and expect the United States-Soviet contest to continue forever." He calls them "the paramilitary—civilian soldiers."

The guilt of killing is spread so thin—shared so universally—that it no longer seems personal. Would the General who pressed the button launching an ICBM be more guilty than the sergeant who helped prepare it for firing? Or the physicist who designed the guidance system? Or the mathematician who programmed the computer? Or the worker who poured concrete for the missile's underground silo? Or the Chicago wife working in a factory who soldered together electrical components for the guidance system?

Was ever the taking of life so clinical, so aseptic, so far removed from personal blame?

No one, then, is responsible—and everyone is responsible. We cannot single out the scientists, or the politicians, or even the military, as the villains of our danger. We have no recourse but the hard one of untangling the hypnotic skein in which we are all enmeshed—of finding a way out to rationality. For even in its own terms, as we shall see, the strategy of enforcing peace through terror is shot through with fallacies and contradictions.

# 3

## *The Family of Bombs*

The birth of the A-bomb temporarily stunned everyone's imagination. An explosion that could flatten seven square miles of a city, as it did at Hiroshima, seemed just about the last word in destructiveness. Even the scientists who had built the bomb were too awed to think of it as only a baby. I recall that when I wrote a newspaper article in the fall of 1946 discussing the possibility of a 50-kiloton bomb—two and a half times more powerful than the Hiroshima weapon —it created such a sensation that the War Department General Staff reprinted it for military circulation.

Yet in less than 20 years, a shorter time than a single human generation, the family of nuclear weapons has grown to unfamilylike proportions. It now includes gigantic offspring which multiply the power of the first-born 5,000-fold. It has become a numerous tribe of weapons in all sorts of calibers, sizes, weights, and shapes. They range from bazooka-shells small enough to be carried by hand to monsters transportable only by a ship—from just a few TNT-tons of power to many millions of tons. What we have had is a veritable "population explosion" of nuclear weapons.

To understand the nature of these weapons we must go back to the physical principles from which the first A-bombs evolved. I do not propose to retell the story of the Manhattan Project but merely to touch upon the fundamentals that underlay the development of various species of bombs.

The making of the atomic bomb depended on solving two basic and different problems, both very difficult. The first was to extract from nature the rather scarce and special fuel. The second was to produce an explosion with this fuel —under control and at the right time.

The primary material, of course, was uranium. Obtaining natural uranium was no problem; the Manhattan Project was able to get substantial amounts of high-grade uranium ore from the Shinkolobwe mines in the Belgian Congo. The first requirement was to refine the uranium to very high purity, something that had never been done before. Pure uranium is a silvery white metal about 50 per cent heavier than lead. It is fissionable, which is to say that its atoms can be made to split with a large release of energy. But natural uranium, no matter how pure, will not itself sustain a chain reaction. We may say that the splitting of one atom in a bar of this material is not so contagious that it infects the rest of the atoms.

Some of the atoms, however, are more susceptible to infection than others. This vulnerable species is known as

24

uranium 235, or simply U-235. Under the right conditions U-235 will split readily when attacked by a neutron, the "virus" of infection. It then releases more neutrons which infect its neighbors. The fever spreads rapidly throughout a whole mass of U-235 atoms.

The problem, then, was to separate the U-235 isotope from natural uranium, where only one atom in every 140 is U-235. This was done by methods that don't need to concern us here; we touch on them in a later chapter. The separation of fissionable U-235 is a very expensive affair: it accounted for about half of the $2 billion spent on the Manhattan Project during the war. Immense plants (incongruously huge compared to the dimensions of the atoms they were processing) were required to produce a few pounds of U-235 per day. They consumed large amounts of electrical power. And for efficiency of extraction, the expensively purified natural uranium had to be discarded after only about half of its U-235 content was winnowed out.

The other major problem that had to be solved was the formation of the bomb. A pound of U-235 makes a sphere about the size of a golf ball. This amount of the stuff is not explosive; aside from radioactivity, it is much safer to handle than TNT. The reason is that it will not sustain a chain reaction, because too many neutrons escape from the surface of the small mass. To achieve a chain reaction you have to put together a "critical mass," large enough to hold in a supply of neutrons which will fission a substantial proportion of the atoms. The critical mass is about ten pounds; if it is jacketed with a material that helps to imprison the neutrons, it may be less. A uranium mass of this weight is roughly the size of a baseball.

The trick in making a bomb is to create a mechanism which will trigger an explosion by bringing the critical mass together suddenly. That was the assignment given to the Los Alamos Laboratory during the war. While the huge production plants at Oak Ridge and Hanford went to work to produce enough fissionable material for a bomb, the Los Alamos Laboratory was built on a mesa near Santa Fe, New Mexico, and a galaxy of scientists and technicians was assembled to experiment on bomb designs, under the direction of Dr. Oppenheimer. It included theoretical and experimental physicists, mathematicians, metallurgists, chemists, electronics experts, engineers, and ordnance specialists.

There were many possible designs for a fission bomb. The one that the Los Alamos group worked out for the first test explosion at Alamogordo was a hollow sphere, called "the Fat Man." Its fissionable material was in the form of a spherical shell with a cavity in the center. Around this material was a thicker shell of ordinary chemical explosive, divided into segments. An electric pulse fired all the segments simultaneously, and the result was an inward blast, or "implosion," which collapsed the sphere into a dense mass. This now-critical mass instantly produced a nuclear explosion.

Theoretically each pound of fissionable material can release energy equivalent to 8,000 tons of TNT; actually the yield of the first bombs was a great deal lower, since much of the material was blown apart before it could fission. Nonetheless, the first explosions amounted to 20,000 TNT tons, or 20 "kilotons." In other words, the yield from the ten pounds of nuclear explosive was 2,000 tons per pound. Of course, in terms of the total weight of the bomb, the yield-to-weight ratio was much less. Altogether, with the chemical explosive, internal structures, and bomb casing, the Hiroshima bomb, for example, weighed some 9,000 pounds. This meant a yield of about two tons of explosion per pound of bomb weight. That was still 4,000 times the yield that can be obtained from a pound of TNT.

The Alamogordo and Nagasaki bombs used U-235 as the nuclear explosive; in the Hiroshima bomb the fissionable material was plutonium, which I will discuss in a later chapter.

The abrupt end of World War II also temporarily ended the driving pressure for development of the nuclear weapons. Most of the scientists at Los Alamos left to return to their universities. Some testing of bomb designs continued: two were exploded in 1946 and three more at Eniwetok in 1948. One of these gave a yield of 50 kilotons. But in these first few relatively quiet years after the war there were no drastic advances in bomb design or yield.

The interlude was short, however. Two developments soon brought about an intense revival of experimenting with nuclear weapons. One was the never-ending rivalry among the United States military services. The other was the Soviet Union's explosion of its first atomic bomb in August of 1949.

The Hiroshima type of bomb was strictly an Air Force weapon: it had to be delivered by heavy bomber. The Air Force succeeded for several years in keeping the weapon to itself. But the Navy and the Army developed an increasing interest in arming themselves with nuclear weapons; the Navy visualized a smaller bomb to be delivered by its carrier-based planes, and the Army a nuclear shell for its artillery. Both services, therefore, wanted experiments toward making smaller, lighter nuclear explosives. Under the astute guidance of Rear Admiral W. S. Parsons, the Navy managed to "infiltrate" the Los Alamos Laboratory and initiate such experiments.

In 1951 the Atomic Energy Commission carried out a series of tests (called Operation Ranger and Operation Buster-Jangle) looking toward the creation of small nuclear weapons. At its Nevada testing site it exploded twelve devices ranging in yield from one to 30 kilotons. Out of these tests, the Army eventually got its nuclear artillery shell, which was proved out during the Upshot-Knothole tests of 1953. This weapon was of dubious military value, for the 280-millimeter shell required a special cannon of dinosaur proportions—a sitting target for enemy fire. However, the research on reducing the size of nuclear devices opened a whole new field of tactical weapons. The upshot of well over a hundred tests was the addition of many small weapons to the nuclear family, including Davy Crockett, the bazooka-shell. The low end of the nuclear-weapons spectrum was extended until it overlapped chemical explosives: some had a yield as low as one ton of TNT.

It may be wondered how a nuclear explosive can be made to give such a low yield, in view of the fact that the fissionable mass must have at least the critical size for an explosion. The answer is that you simply make the mechanism very inefficient, so that the chain reaction affects only a small part of the material.

At the upper end of the spectrum, A-bombs were developed to considerably higher yields than 50 kilotons. But there is a limit to the practicable size of a fission bomb. Not only do the physical and technical problems become very difficult as the bomb gets bigger, but the cost in fuel rises astronomically. Fissionable material (U-235 or plutonium) now runs about $6,000 a pound (it was much higher at the beginning). Assuming 50 per cent efficiency in explosive yield (*i.e.*, four kilotons per pound), the cost of the fuel is $1,500 per kiloton of explosion. For a one-megaton bomb (a million tons, or 1,000 kilotons) the fuel cost would be $1.5 million. This may not be a high price in terms of military budgets, but it is very high in terms of the number of pounds of fissionable material it would call for. One such bomb would require as much as 50 bombs of the Hiroshima type—and produce far less destruction than the 50.

When the U.S.S.R. broke the United States A-bomb monopoly in 1949, the thoughts of the military and its advisers turned in another direction. To keep its lead, they felt, the United States must develop still more powerful weapons. The direction to which they turned was Dr. Edward Teller and his plea for development of an H-bomb.

The fusion of hydrogen, as a source of nuclear energy, had been discovered by physicists even before fission. Hans Bethe had deduced in 1938 that this was the process that generated the heat and light of the sun. In the early 1940s Dr. Teller, a Hungarian-born physicist who had come to the United States in 1935, began to ruminate on the possibilities of making a bomb based on fusion. He was working at Columbia with the great Italian physicist Enrico Fermi. Fermi, who was later to become a leader in the Manhattan Project, suggested to Teller that the fusion of hydrogen might be achieved most easily by using the rare isotope of hydrogen called deuterium. (The isotope had been discovered in 1932 by the Columbia chemist Harold Urey. Asked at the time whether he thought any practical use would ever be found for deuterium, Urey suggested that it might be a useful research tool, like the rare gas xenon. "This must go down in history," Urey remarked to me recently with a chuckle, "as the greatest scientific misestimate ever made.")

After skirmishing briefly with the fusion problem at Columbia, Teller joined the theoretical physicists in the

Manhattan Project. While they concentrated on the fission-bomb problem, Teller's heart remained in the fusion bomb, which he called "Super." But at the Los Alamos Laboratory, where he was working, Project Super was put aside for the A-bomb. As Teller relates it: "We had to win the war and there was no time for the Super."

In fact, as it turned out, the Super would have been impossible without the A-bomb, for on the earth only the A-bomb produces a flame hot enough to kindle a fusion chain reaction.

In the fall of 1949, following the shock of the Soviet A-bomb, Teller at last gained attention in the highest circles for his Super. Behind closed doors, a fierce debate began on whether a crash program to make the H-bomb should be undertaken; it involved scientists, the Atomic Energy Commission, the Joint Committee on Atomic Energy, and President Truman. The argument might never have emerged into the open, had not the late Senator Edwin C. Johnson, a member of the Joint Committee, broken security by blurting it out on television. "Here's the thing that is top secret," he announced to a startled nation on the night of November 1, 1949, and he went on to disclose the proposal for a weapon 1,000 times more powerful than the Nagasaki bomb.

Bethe and many of his fellow scientists were strongly opposed to the H-bomb project, on both moral and practical grounds. But, unlike the politicians, they were severely hampered in discussing the issue in public, because of secrecy restrictions on them. Consequently the technical and strategic questions involved never received the full public airing that should have been given to so important a decision.

For President Truman, who made the final decision, there were no agonizing doubts. Only one course was possible: "We must keep ahead." What would be the situation of the United States if the Russians made an H-bomb and the United States were caught unprepared? On January 31, 1950, the President ordered the Atomic Energy Commission to proceed with all speed on H-bomb research.

To scientists of sensitive conscience such as Dr. Bethe, it was a melancholy order. As Bethe said in retrospect years afterward:

> "The scientist looked into the hell of the bomb long before anybody else did. One of the things that trouble me is that nobody believes us when we predict the hell, and that even the responses we scientists make . . . are not appropriate to the magnitude of that hell. The response the Government made in 1949 and 1950 to go ahead and develop the bomb was natural and perhaps even correct. It was said then that we were in a Cold War and we had to develop the hydrogen bomb because the Russians would develop it. Well, they sure did, but it was obvious that there would be no security. And I think it is obvious now that weapons are completely out of proportion, that they no longer have any function as a continuation of foreign policy."

In 1950 it was far from clear that this fearsome weapon could actually be built. Indeed, the H-bomb envisioned at that time never *was* built. As the Los Alamos scientists proceeded with their studies of the fusion device they had in mind, the project looked more and more hopeless. The bomb eventually became possible only through a radical change in approach.

In principle the achievement of the H-bomb reaction hinged upon using an A-bomb to produce a multimillion-degree temperature which would ignite a fusion chain reaction in a mass of hydrogen composing the core of the bomb. As Fermi had suggested, ordinary hydrogen was not suitable; deuterium offered a better chance for fusion. But now it appeared that even deuterium was not sufficient; the bomb required a still more fusible—and rarer—hydrogen isotope, namely, tritium. This triple-weight form of hydrogen is so rare in Nature that it would have to be manufactured.

Tritium can be produced by bombarding the light element lithium in a reactor with neutrons, which split the lithium nucleus and yield tritium as one of the fragments. Even before a bomb was designed, the Atomic Energy Commission prepared to build huge reactors on the Savannah River in South Carolina to manufacture tritium. From the standpoint of the economy of weapons-making, however, this in itself was a questionable move, because reactors could be used more effectively to produce plutonium for A-bombs.

But the main difficulty with the H-bomb idea was a matter of physics. How could the fuel charge be held together to sustain a chain reaction? When tritium and deuterium fuse, they produce helium and release neutrons. Most of the energy from the fusion reaction is contained in the high speed of the ejected neutrons. This is a very slippery thing to capture. Whereas in the fission of uranium the high-speed fragments in the dense mass quickly collide and produce heat, in the hydrogen reaction the energetic, light, uncharged neutrons easily pass through the surrounding hydrogen atoms and carry off their energy into the air.

In the spring of 1951 Dr. Teller came forth with a new approach to the bomb. He presented it at a meeting of the experts on the project in Princeton. Striding up and down before a much-chalked blackboard, Teller enthusiastically explained his idea. Just what his breakthrough was has never been publicly specified. But Dr. Bethe, who was present, described it afterward as "a brilliant discovery . . . a stroke of genius which does not occur in the normal development of ideas."

At precisely 7:14 on the morning of November 1, 1952, the world was catapulted into the hydrogen era—though most of the world was not aware of the event until sometime later. On a tiny sandspit in the Pacific Ocean the Atomic Energy Commission made a secret test of its first hydrogen device. Code-named *Mike*, it was a 50-ton affair in the form of a cubical box 25 feet on edge—the size of a two-story house. Its hydrogen fuel was condensed, by means of refrigeration, into the densest possible form—liquefied hydrogen. This was to be touched off to explode by a huge A-bomb.

The "shot island" was a coral spit named Elugelab, in the Eniwetok atoll. The firing center was on another island 20 miles away, manned by a crew crouched inside a concrete shelter. A fleet of naval vessels and observers in planes, well-distanced from Elugelab, tensely waited for the shot. Some of the scientists prayed that the experiment would show the H-bomb was not a feasible proposition.

At 7:14 the gadget was detonated. A bluish-white flash of light lit up hundreds of miles of the Pacific. Almost instantly a huge fireball engulfed the little island. It was as if a giant hand had dropped on it a piece scooped out of the blazing sun. The fireball swelled rapidly, like a monstrous, incarnate tumor growing from the earth. It rested briefly on the surface, then slowly detached itself and roared upward, sucking up millions of tons of coral and water turned to steam. The flaming ball grew to a helmet-shaped inferno more than three miles in diameter. Gradually it cooled to a vast cloud in the sky 100,000 feet above the site, and the cloud began to drift downwind and disperse.

The islet of Elugelab had vanished. In its place was a sea-filled cavity 175 feet deep and a mile in diameter. An adjoining islet was wiped clean of everything on its surface; nothing built by man could have survived on it.

Thousands of miles away, in a darkened basement room of the University of California in Berkeley, Dr. Teller was watching the dancing beam of light of a seismograph. About 15 minutes after the shot at Elugelab, the gently undulating beam suddenly jumped wildly, signaling the arrival of the violent earth tremors. The experiment had worked; the thermonuclear age was born!

Within nine months the Soviet Union, not to be outdone, also produced a thermonuclear explosion. Both contestants proceeded to translate this new power into weapons.

The *Mike* shot amounted to some twelve megatons— twelve million tons of TNT. It was not, however, a military weapon; the bulky experimental contrivance had to be reduced to the dimensions of a deliverable bomb. Seventeen months after *Mike*, the H-bomb was produced and tested.

On March 15, 1954, the Atomic Energy Commission began a series of tests ("Operation Castle") in the Bikini area of the Marshall Islands. Its first shot was called *Bravo*. This time the world heard of the explosion almost immediately, for some of its radioactive ashes fell upon 23 Japanese fishermen in a tuna trawler named the *Lucky Dragon*. *Bravo*, fired on a metal tower in the Bikini lagoon, yielded 15 megatons. It disclosed several points of scientific and technical interest.

The fusion fuel was not liquid hydrogen but a much more compact and efficient package: a solid compound called lithium deuteride, composed of lithium and deuterium. The lithium used was an uncommon isotope known as lithium 6, which is fairly easily split by neutrons. When it splits, one of the fragments is tritium. Thus the bomb generated its own fuel; it was unnecessary to manufacture tritium at great expense in a reactor. Excited to high energy in the heat of the A-bomb trigger, the tritium fused with the deuterium. And the reaction produced a copious supply of neutrons to spark the explosion of the whole mass of fuel.

Another potent ingredient was present in the bomb. It was enclosed in a heavy jacket of ordinary uranium. This served not only to block the high-energy neutrons from escaping but also to augment the explosion. The common isotope of uranium, U-238, does not fission nearly as readily as U-235; therefore it will not itself sustain a chain reaction. But it can be fissioned by very fast neutrons. The great swarm of energetic neutrons released by the fusing hydrogen succeeded in fissioning a substantial part of the U-238 jacket, not as a chain reaction but as a shotgun effect. Thus the U-238 became part of the fuel and multiplied the power of the bomb.

The switch to lithium and U-238 as explosive fuels elevated nuclear bomb-making to a new level of power. It made nuclear bombs far cheaper per megaton of yield. And simply by adding ordinary uranium one could make a bomb as big and powerful as one pleased.

The race between the United States and the U.S.S.R. to outmatch each other in nuclear firepower did not slacken; instead, it speeded up. From 1954 through 1958 the testing of new weapons went on at an accelerating pace. By November of 1958 the nuclear powers (including Great Britain) had detonated, *in tests alone,* more than 100 times as much explosive power as the total dropped on Germany in all the bombing raids of World War II. The megatonnage exploded was equal to the total body weight of the entire human population of the earth.

The moratorium on testing that the nuclear powers undertook at the end of 1958 stopped the explosions, but not the research on weapons. When the moratorium was broken by the Soviet Union in the fall of 1961, a new phase in the aggrandizement of the bomb began. Premier Nikita Khrushchev announced:

> "Let those who dream of new aggression know that we shall have a bomb equal in capacity to 100 million tons of TNT, that we already have such a bomb and shall test the explosive device for it."

On October 23 Mr. Khrushchev exploded the first of his new bombs. The United States long-range detection network noted that the explosion took place fairly low in the atmosphere above the Soviet proving grounds at Novaya Zemlya in the arctic region. Its power was estimated to be 25 megatons. A week later the Soviet weapons makers let go with the biggest blast in the world's history. This one amounted to 58 megatons. Its power was nearly one-third as great as the total of all the nuclear bombs exploded in the world up to 1958.

Set off at an altitude of only 12,000 feet, the 58-megatonner was expected to produce a fantastic downwind fallout. But the Russians had a surprise for the Western experts. When United States scientists analyzed samples of the bomb debris (which had been scooped up in the atmosphere by high-flying aircraft), they learned that: (1) the bomb had been encased in a lead jacket, and (2) less than 2 per cent of its energy had come from fission, the rest from fusion. As a result, it was an extraordinarily "clean" bomb, with relatively little fallout.

Dr. Bethe was quick to note that if the bomb had been encased in uranium instead of lead, the yield might well have been more than 100 megatons. Thus the Soviet testers had actually proved out the design of a potential 100-megatonner, merely substituting lead for uranium to minimize contamination of the atmosphere.

The Soviet tests demonstrated what United States bomb experts had already realized: that the thermonuclear bomb was an "open-ended" affair, meaning that it could be built to any size, and at comparatively little extra cost. With lithium deuteride and ordinary uranium as the supplementary fuel, the cost per megaton of a nuclear bomb decreases sharply as the size increases. The scale runs something like this: it costs $750,000 for a 100,000-ton explosion (A-bomb type), $1 million for one megaton (H-bomb), $1.1 million for ten megatons, and $1.2 million for 100 megatons. In other words, above ten megatons the cost is only a penny or less for each additional ton of explosive power.

The efficiency of the yield per pound of bomb weight also increases, because fusion fuel, pound for pound, can produce three times more explosive power than fission fuel. It can be estimated that a bomb in the range above 20 megatons could yield four kilotons or more per pound of bomb weight—double the efficiency of a smaller bomb. On this basis, a 100-megaton bomb would weigh some 15 tons. Such a bomb could be carried by a heavy bomber, though not by present ICBMs.

We have seen nuclear weapons grow, then, by thousand-fold jumps—from kilotons to megatons. There appears to be nothing to bar another such jump—from megatons to thousand-megatons, or what we might call the "gigaton." Such a weapon could be made without bursting the seams of today's technology. The "G-bomb" might weigh somewhere between 100 and 200 tons. It would not be deliverable by bomber or ballistic missile, but it could sail into a harbor aboard a ship or stand off a country's coast as a threat. And some day it might be assembled in space as a veritable Damoclean sword hovering over a nation's head.

The monstrous multi-megaton bombs have already passed the limits of reason. What possible military purpose could they serve? Even the generals consider them excessive. General Curtis E. LeMay, chief of the United States Air Force, retorted after Khrushchev's boast of a 100-megaton bomb that the United States could have built one "if it had wanted one." Assistant Secretary of Defense Paul H. Nitze observed that we already had "a tremendous variety of warheads which gives us the flexibility we require to conduct nuclear actions from the level of large-scale destruction to mere demolition work."

The hideous fact is that the giant bombs have grown beyond being instruments of warfare and have become psychological weapons—a means of striking terror, of intimidating whole populations. The mere hint of possession of such weapons is enough to paralyze nations and alter drastically the whole basis of international relations.

In the next two chapters, let us investigate the dimensions of the threat in more detail.

# 4

# *The Incredible Stockpile*

The Prussian military philosopher Karl von Clausewitz in the early nineteenth century handed down the dictum: "War is an act of force, and to the application of that force there is no limit." In Clausewitz's time this was no more than a form of literary hyperbole, but he was a prophet ahead of his time. His figure of speech has become literal truth: in the 1960s it can accurately be said that we are possessed of military force which for all practical purposes is unlimited. The stockpile of nuclear weapons has grown to a size sufficient to dispose of life on this planet in short order.

For reasons that defy logic, the magnitude of the stockpile is a fanatically guarded secret. Probably no more than a handful of men in the highest circles of our Government are entrusted with knowledge of the size of the United States stockpile, and to divulge the secret would no doubt be regarded as the most treasonous of crimes. Paradoxically, the policy of supersecrecy here runs directly counter to the professed reason for accumulating the stockpile. If the purpose is to prevent war by threatening any aggressor with overwhelming retaliation, then the rational course would seem to be to advertise, rather than conceal, the size of this striking power!

However one looks at it, no reasonable person can escape the conclusion that the secrecy policy is a kind of fetish. Former President Harry S. Truman has written in his *Memoirs*: ". . . in no document in my office, in the AEC, or anywhere in Government, could anyone find the exact number of bombs in stockpile, or the number of bombs to be produced, or the amount of material scheduled for production." Yet every physicist knows that any expert in nuclear weaponry, friend or foe, could make approximately accurate estimates on all these quantities by analyzing published information.

In 1953 I undertook to assess the size of the United States nuclear stockpile for a book on which I collaborated with Stewart and Joseph Alsop. The key to such an estimate lay, of course, in trying to calculate the probable output of fissionable material by the big plants at Oak Ridge in Tennessee and Hanford in the State of Washington. To project the size the stockpile might attain by 1960, I also took into account other plants the AEC was building for production of A-bomb material. (At the time, the H-bomb could not be reckoned as a weapon.)

I recalled a comment by the late Senator Brien Mc-

Mahon, author of the Atomic Energy Act and a member of the Joint Congressional Committee, after he was told how many bombs were in the stockpile. "The size of the stockpile," he said, "can be estimated to within 15 per cent." This implied, of course, that the estimate could be based on the known methods of producing fissionables.

I dug through my extensive files of Congressional hearings and collected the vital statistics about our nuclear plants. There were four promising ways of estimating the amount of their production. It might be calculated from: (1) the amount of uranium feed material flowing into the plants, (2) the amount of electric power the plants used, (3) the capital investment in the plants, or (4) the annual sums spent for operation of the plants. The year-by-year increase in each of these figures should give four independent indexes of the increase in production.

The actual figures, of course, were not public, and there were few definite signposts for guidance. But from the available information it was possible to arrive at rough estimates of the rate of growth in each of the four indexes. It turned out that all four gave about the same result—a surprisingly good check on the reliability of my calculations. Using this estimate of the rate of growth, I then plotted on blue graph-paper a curve for the rise in production of fissionable material from 1945, when only a few pounds were produced per day, to 1960, taking into account new plants which were expected to be in full production by that time.

According to this curve, by the end of 1960 the stockpile of fissionable material would total some 350 *tons* (with a possible error of 20 per cent more or less). The 350 tons would be the equivalent of 70,000 Hiroshima bombs! And remember that this projection was based on production capacities in 1953 and did not include the H-bomb at all.

The production of fissionable material started out (during the war) with two plants: the Oak Ridge facilities for separating U-235 and the Hanford reactors for manufacturing plutonium.

At Oak Ridge the main output came from the gaseous-diffusion process. Uranium in a gaseous form (uranium hexafluoride) was pumped through a "porous" barrier in which the pores were so tiny that a pin-prick would be considered a yawning hole. U-235 passed through the barrier at a slightly better rate than the heavier U-238. The uranium gas was pumped through myriads of barriers until its U-235 content was enriched to better than 95 per cent.

The wartime production at Oak Ridge was a mere trickle of U-235—less than one ton per year. In the postwar years these diffusion plants were expanded three times, eventually totaling a plant investment of more than $1 billion. In addition, huge new gaseous-diffusion facilities were built in the early 1950s at Paducah, Kentucky, and Portsmouth, Ohio.

Meanwhile the production of plutonium was undergoing a similar expansion. Early in the research on fissionable explosives, experiments had established that plutonium would serve as well as U-235 as bomb material. It could be formed from the common isotope of uranium, U-238, in a controlled, graphite-moderated reactor, then known as a "pile." In such a reactor, neutrons from fissions of U-235 atoms are absorbed by U-238 atoms and transform them to a new element, neptunium, which quickly transforms itself (by emitting a particle) into plutonium, element number 94. Plutonium, unlike other artificial heavy elements, is fairly stable, with a half-life of 24,000 years. After a certain proportion of the U-238 in the uranium rods has been converted to plutonium, the rods are removed from the pile and the plutonium is extracted from them chemically.

During the war three huge plutonium-producing reactors were built at Hanford on the Columbia River in Washington. The capital investment in them was half a billion dollars. In the 1950s a vast new production center with five reactors (originally planned to make tritium, as we have seen) was constructed on the Savannah River in South Carolina. This complex represented an investment of more than $1 billion.

The investment in plants for production of fissionable material has grown, then, to some $5.5 billion, and production is going on night and day at five major centers—Oak Ridge, Hanford, Paducah, Portsmouth, and Savannah.

The rate of operation of these plants can be judged from the fact that the three centers turning out U-235 use 5.8 million kilowatts of electricity and burn a thousand carloads of coal each day. In 1960 the AEC's total bill for electricity was a quarter of a billion dollars.

The consumption of uranium raw material is on the same scale. From about 2,000 tons of uranium a year in the late 1940s, it has jumped to more than 30,000 tons per year. In 1961 uranium mines in the United States alone (at some 900 sites) delivered 17,410 tons of uranium oxide to the AEC. Uranium mining has become a huge new industry, complete with pressure lobby.

Altogether the United States outlay for nuclear explosives runs to nearly $2 billion per year. Apparently there has been no slackening of production. By 1967, at the present rate, the fissionable stockpile will reach some 1,000 tons— equal to 200,000 Hiroshima bombs! Bear in mind that this material may be used as a trigger for H-bombs, which multiply the explosive power many times. One can estimate conservatively that the United States stockpile of nuclear bombs, including H-bombs, already amounts to at least 30,-000 megatons, enough to saturate a continent—or to over-kill the Soviet Union many times.

Early in 1960 John F. Kennedy, then a United States Senator, said in a speech at the University of New Hampshire: "The world's nuclear stockpile contains, it is estimated, the equivalent of 30 billion tons of TNT—about ten tons of TNT for every human being on the globe." In view of the continued production since then, and the Soviet tests of super-superbombs in 1961, the explosive quota per human being must now be considerably higher. The explosion of the weapons stockpile is proceeding at a faster rate than the world population explosion.

How has this monstrous growth got so out of hand—this non-stop, seemingly unstoppable construction of a Frankenstein that mankind goes on building with ever-increasing compulsiveness as the monster grows more frightening?

In part the reasons are quite innocent and matter-of-fact. We Americans have a mania for mass production and accumulating surpluses—whether in autos, wheat, or weapons. The economy of weapons-making has its own inertial momentum: budgets are spent, contracts are fulfilled, job-holders preserve their jobs, without reference to the nature of what they are producing. Whether their product rots in warehouses or cripples the human race is, in this sense, a matter of indifference. Weapons-making makes work, and jobs keep job-holders in office. This factor alone makes an arms race hard to stop.

In part, also, the uncontrolled growth of the stockpile

has been simply a function of secrecy. Few Americans, even in Congress, have any clear picture of its absurd proportions. General debate of the subject is foreclosed in the first instance by lack of knowledge.

What must be considered most alarming is that even at the highest levels of decision the continued building of the stockpile seems to have a quality of inevitability. From the beginning, United States political leaders, under strong pressure from the Cold War-minded press, have seen only one politically safe course: namely, to make the United States all-powerful in nuclear arms—to "keep ahead." Even more ardently than the military, they have called for bigger and bigger programs.

After the Atomic Energy Commission was set up as the nation's chief munitions producer after the war, the long-range objective assigned to it was a stockpile of 50 tons of fissionable explosive—the equivalent of more than 10,000 Hiroshima bombs. The Soviet achievement of an A-bomb in 1949 and the Korean war touched off in Congress a loud demand for drastic upgrading of this goal. Two military reasons were advanced for a bigger stockpile: (1) the policy of "massive retaliation" to deter an attack by the Soviet Union called for an arsenal sufficient to destroy that country, and (2) tactical nuclear weapons were needed for fighting smaller wars such as Korea. Such weapons, depending entirely on fissionable explosive, would be a heavier drain on the stockpile than H-bombs.

In the fall of 1951 Senator McMahon introduced a resolution in the Senate calling for a vast expansion of the AEC production program. A fellow member of the Joint Committee on Atomic Energy, then Representative Henry Jackson (later a Senator), joined vigorously in this demand. He asked for $6 billion to $10 billion a year to build "atomic weapons in huge quantities and great varieties." The Representative went on:

> "The real peddlers of military nostrums are those who imagine that the atom bomb can be decisive in warfare without producing it by the thousands and tens of thousands. Tactical uses of atomic energy alone will profitably absorb all the atomic weapons it is within our power to turn out."

Historians of the future who investigate the etiology of the rise of the United States atomic stockpile will no doubt find their richest material in the files of the Joint Committee on Atomic Energy. It was this Committee of 18 men—not the AEC itself or even the Department of Defense—that took the lead in expanding the program of weapons-building. It initiated the great expansion of production in the early 1950s which is still rolling on with undiminished vigor.

The late Gordon Dean, then chairman of the AEC, who was in the best of all positions to know what the expansion meant, was so disturbed that he urged that the public be given "some idea of the magnitude of our stockpile and its tremendous destructive potential." On September 17, 1952, addressing the American Bar Association at San Francisco, he raised a question which few men had the courage to voice:

> "I think it is quite obvious that the current atomic arms race cannot go on forever. Somewhere along the line there is a point where the law of diminishing returns begins to operate. And somewhere not far beyond this point there is another point where we will have acquired all the weapons we would possibly need to destroy not only the industrial ability of an aggressor to make war but also his forces in the field.
> "When this point is reached, and it is *not* in the *unforeseeable* future, the question arises: What do we do then? Do

we go on turning out more and more fissionable material and more and more weapons, as we are doing now? Or do we say to ourselves: 'Now we have enough; no matter how many bombs our competitor may choose to make, we have enough.'

". . . does it achieve any more deterrence, or does it enhance our chances in the event of war, to have enough to defeat him and his armies 20 times over?"

Mr. Dean, an eminent lawyer and investment banker, was killed in an aircraft accident near Martha's Vineyard in 1958. He had left the AEC in 1953 and was succeeded as chairman by Lewis L. Strauss. Neither Strauss nor his successors ever saw fit to re-ask Dean's question, at least in public.

There are those who argue that the great overproduction of fissionable material is not sheer waste, because the surplus can be used for peaceful purposes. The United States has pledged more than 40 tons from the stockpile to fuel nuclear reactors abroad. Some of the AEC's supply has also been allocated to power reactors for producing electricity in the United States and to nuclear-powered ships. But all possible diversions for such purposes would make only a small dent in the gigantic military stockpile. And in any event, the question of waste is secondary to the central fact that the existence of this vast stockpile for destruction represents insecurity and mortal danger for the whole world. Piling up more tons of bomb material, more thousands of bombs, does not add to the national security of the United States.

# 5

## *Blast, Fire, and Fallout*

In round numbers some 350 nuclear explosions have been detonated by the nuclear powers since 1945. Many of the tests were performed for the specific purpose of studying the effects of such explosions. Yet no aspect of nuclear weapons is surrounded with more confusion and misinformation. For this state of affairs the AEC itself seems to be primarily responsible. It has been extremely secretive on important features of the weapon effects, and those reports it has issued from time to time have been technical and far from candid. The AEC has consistently minimized the effects, particularly from fallout.

In the spring of 1962 the AEC and the Defense Depart-

49

ment published a 730-page book titled *The Effects of Nuclear Weapons,* explaining in a foreword:

> "There is a need for widespread public understanding of the best information available on the effects of nuclear weapons. The purpose of this book is to present as accurately as possible, within the limits of national security, a comprehensive summary of this information."

Within the limits of unclassified knowledge, I will try to summarize briefly the known facts, analyzing what this publication had to say—and what it failed to say.

We must think in terms of megaton bombs, for these are now the standard weapons. Unfortunately the Government report (which we'll call *Effects*) does not discuss explosions above 20 megatons. We must therefore extrapolate from the given data to estimate the effects of bigger bombs.

Let us consider first the blast effects. A city, viewed as the object of a megaton attack, is largely a "soft" target. Its core is a closely clustered collection of medium-hard, high-rise buildings, and around this lies a widely sprawling aggregation of small dwellings. In a city such as Detroit, Chicago, or Buffalo this consists of mile after mile of wooden frame houses. They are as vulnerable to blast as the flimsy homes of Hiroshima. Their roofs are just strong enough to support a load of snow. A blast pressure of 2.5 pounds per square inch will level such a house; 10 psi (pounds per square inch) will blow it to bits, as AEC tests in its Nevada proving grounds have demonstrated.

A one-megaton bomb exploded at low altitude would crush every wooden house within six miles of the burst; a ten-megatonner would destroy all within 14 miles; and a 100-megatonner would extend this destruction out to about

30 miles. This means that if a 100-megaton bomb were dropped on, say, Manhattan, the blast alone would also flatten most of the houses of Westchester and the suburbs of Long Island and northern New Jersey.

For brick apartment houses, the ranges of destruction ("severe damage" in the parlance of blast experts) are four miles from a one-megaton explosion, nine miles from a ten-megaton, and 18 miles from a 100-megaton. As for sturdier office buildings, a one-megaton bomb would knock down all within three miles, and a 100-megatonner would level all within a twelve-mile radius. Ordinary shelters, capable of withstanding up to 30 psi, would not escape; a one-megatonner would crush those within one mile, and a 100-megatonner all within five miles.

Although the picture of a city crashing in ruins and burying its population under falling beams and brick is not pleasant to contemplate, the *fire* effects of megaton bombs are even more frightening than blast. The first flash of heat from such a bomb would sear every exposed object over a wide area. On a clear day a one-megatonner would produce second-degree burns of the skin as far as nine miles from the burst, a ten-megatonner as far as 24 miles, and a 100-megatonner out to 70 miles. Over nearly as wide a range, the heat flash would ignite wooden houses and other combustibles. Of course, the ranges of ignition would depend on the height of the burst, the terrain, the haziness of the atmosphere, the dryness of the exposed objects, and many other factors.

The initial flash would be only the beginning of the fire damage. World War II introduced the phenomenon of the firestorm in bombed cities; incendiary bombs alone produced such storms in Tokyo, Hamburg, and other targets. When a massive fire is touched off, a hot column of air shoots up from the center of the fire; air then rushes in from all sides and acts like a blow-torch, so that the whole area is saturated with intense flame. In a true firestorm the burning continues until there is essentially nothing left to burn. At Hiroshima the firestorm started by the A-bomb generated winds of 30 to 40 miles per hour and burned out an area of nearly five square miles in twelve hours. The ruins smoldered for three days.

The firestorm phenomenon may represent the greatest single killing factor in the megaton-bombing of a city. The fire goes on building up after the explosion until it reaches a peak hours afterward. It burns up the oxygen in the area of the storm, so that even people in deep shelters would be asphyxiated unless they had stored oxygen supplies. Moreover, the fire enveloping a bombed city would trap the population, preventing evacuation or any organized rescue operations.

We have little information on which to base an estimate of just how severe the fire effects of a multimegaton explosion would be, and not much is known about the firestorm phenomenon itself; the *Effects* report devotes only a page and a quarter to it. Some persons have speculated that firestorms from a superbomb attack might burn out vast areas of the country. Gerard Piel, the talented publisher of *Scientific American,* asserted in a speech in 1961 that, "according to one set of calculations," a 1,000-megaton bomb exploded at very high altitude could set afire six Western states. This seems unlikely (even if we assume that so large a bomb could be sent aloft). From what we know about the firestorm phenomenon, it appears that it would be limited to the central parts of cities; firestorms probably could not develop in the less densely built suburbs or small towns.

There is not much doubt, however, that the major cities in the area of attack would be burned to the ground.

Much would depend on how the attacker chose to use his superbombs. If he wanted to maximize the fire effects, he would explode the bombs at very high altitude; to maximize blast and radiation effects, he would set them off at low altitude. Incidentally, let us note that the defender must worry about a fire hazard of his own creation. If he uses megaton bombs to intercept attacking ICBMs, he may expose large areas of his own country to heat flash.

A not-insignificant aspect of this flash is the hazard to the eyesight of the population. Anyone who happened to look directly at a megaton burst, even from hundreds of miles away, might be blinded. An experiment performed with rabbits as subjects in 1958 showed that a bomb exploded at an altitude of about 50 miles would burn the retina of an exposed eye out to slant distances of 345 miles. From explosions at higher altitude, the range of retinal damage would be greater.

The third, and most complex, of the bomb effects is the deadly damage of nuclear radiation. The explosion of any nuclear bomb spews forth a vast flood of gamma rays and neutrons. Gamma rays are well known as the powerful, penetrating radiation emitted by radium and also in the form of X-rays, with which they are identical in properties. In the immediate vicinity of an explosion, the primary flash of this radiation is intense enough to kill anyone not killed by blast or fire. At Hiroshima the lethal radius of the nuclear radiation was about three-quarters of a mile. In the case of a 100-megaton bomb it would be about three miles. The reason this range is so much smaller than for blast and heat is that gamma rays and neutrons are rather quickly absorbed by the atoms in air. In outer space, with no air in the way, a multi-megaton explosion would send forth deadly radiation for a distance of almost a thousand miles.

The really significant radiation danger is not the direct, primary flash (people within its lethal range would be killed anyway by the explosion) but the great shower of radio-active debris from the bomb—that is, fallout. This spreads out over a vast area and goes on emitting its destructive radiation for days, months, and years.

To understand the effects of such radiation we must first specify the units in which it is measured. The basic unit used in reckoning biological effects is the *roentgen*, which measures the absorption of the radiation by living tissue. In effect, the roentgen is a measure of the kill-power of radia-tion, and the yardsticks of exposure are based on this unit.

A dose of less than 100 roentgens usually produces no acute or detectable effects; fortunately so, for otherwise X-rays could not be used in medicine. This does not neces-sarily mean there is no damage at all: in the long run some body cells, and especially germ cells, may show deleterious effects. But under-100 roentgen doses do not make people ill.

A dose between 100 and 200 roentgens will give many people a spell of "radiation sickness." The main symptoms are weakness, nausea, and vomiting. But barring complica-tions, such as infection (to which irradiation makes the body vulnerable), people exposed to such a dose will recover completely within a few days or weeks.

At doses above 200 roentgens, radiation begins to be-come lethal. An exposure between 200 and 300 r will kill some people within a month; 300 to 400 r will kill about one-third of those exposed, unless they receive treatment; and between 400 and 600 r the death rate climbs to 50 per cent or higher. Death does not come immediately. A person exposed to a lethal dose may seem to recover from his radiation sickness after a week or two. But then the symptoms return; he loses his hair; he suffers extreme weakness, bloody diarrhea, bleeding around the gums, and high fever, and dies within a month. If the dose is over 1,000 roentgens, the whole sequence is speeded up; the victim may go into convulsions and behave irrationally soon after his exposure.

Let us keep these figures in mind now as we examine the levels of fallout generated by the nuclear bombs since 1945.

At Hiroshima and Nagasaki the fallout effects were negligible, completely overshadowed by the bomb's immediate destruction. Only a tiny portion of the bomb debris was deposited within the city limits, and the highest dose from this was estimated to be no more than 100 roentgens.

The first test of an A-bomb at Alamogordo had, to be sure, given a small warning of the fallout hazard. The fireball from the shot sucked up sand and dust from the desert floor and inoculated this material with radioactive fission products from the explosion. The radioactive cloud then drifted downwind. Some ten to 15 miles from the explosion site a small herd of cattle was grazing on the scanty desert vegetation. Particles from the bomb cloud, obeying the truism that what goes up must come down, fell upon the herd. The Manhattan Project scientists later found that this "hot" fallout had made blotches on the animals' hides. But the cattle seemed otherwise unharmed, and no one worried very much about the portent.

The phenomenon began to give more serious concern a year later, when an A-bomb was exploded 90 feet underwater in the Bikini lagoon in the test series called Operation Crossroads. The explosion shot up a stubby mushroom cloud of mist that spread out over the lagoon like an ominous rain of poison. I remember watching it from my post on a submarine chaser outside the lagoon and wondering if the dripping cloud would ever stop growing. It drenched the fleet in the lagoon with fission products and radioactive salt. When the sun dried the decks, it left them coated with a largely invisible residue of radioactivity—an indelible inscription of the fallout hazard. The Navy had to abandon the ships, but it had a few of them towed to its Radiological Defense Laboratory at Hunter's Point in San Francisco for study.

The amount of contamination of those ships has never been made public, not even in the 1962 report on *Effects of Nuclear Weapons,* which purports to summarize "the best information available" on weapon effects to promote "public understanding." There is a hint, however, in a Navy report inadvertently released in 1953: this said that the Navy had to be prepared for fallout intensities of up to 10,000 roentgens per hour one hour after an attack.

Although the Navy had the wind up about the fallout hazard, apparently the other services and the AEC did not get the message. At any rate, they remained unperturbed. Five years after the demonstration in the Bikini lagoon, General Elwood R. Quesada, commander of the 1951 tests in the Pacific, told a press conference: "Our operations have indicated to us clearly that the mysterious ghost of lingering radiation should be dispelled." And his radiation safety adviser, Brigadier General James Cooney, said residual radiation hazards after a nuclear attack would be so minor that casualties could be removed without serious danger to the rescuers.

The next encounter with fallout was more alarming than the first two. It came in the *Mike* shot of November 1, 1952—the first H-bomb test. As I mentioned in Chapter 3, this explosion blasted the coral islet of Elugelab out of the sea. Six years later an obscure, tardily issued report told something about the fallout from that shot.

It seems that the winds were expected to sweep the fallout northward over the sea, but instead they blew it southeast over some small islands of the Eniwetok Atoll, fortunately unoccupied. On one of these, called Engebi, within an hour after the explosion the radiation intensity from the fallout rose to 1,000 roentgens per hour, according to instrument readings. A 30-minute visit to that island would have been fatal. Twelve hours after the shot the level was still 200 r per hour. Other islands in the vicinity also were made hot by fallout.

Three times the testers of nuclear weapons had seen disquieting indications of how dangerous a phenomenon fallout might be, yet they remained silent on the subject. The terse public reports of the task forces that had conducted the tests in the Pacific gave no hint of the hazard. Aside from vague references to radioactive contamination in newspaper accounts of the Bikini shots, the public was given little or no information about the fallout phenomenon.

It is hard to understand a secrecy policy that could withhold such vital information, or why the Government and its scientific advisers were so slow to pay any serious attention to the problem. Whatever the reasons, fallout remained a hush-hush phenomenon on which the detailed facts were known only to a few experts engaged in weapons research and testing.

In the summer of 1953 a group of 49 experts—consultants of the AEC, military men, and Government officials—finally was convened by the AEC for a secret discussion of the subject at the headquarters of the RAND Corporation in

Santa Monica, California. (The report of this conference was not made public until 1958, nearly five years after the meeting.) The experts were brought together to consider "Worldwide Effects of Atomic Weapons," and the chief effect that was on their minds was a substance known as strontium 90. This is one of the radioactive fission products of the splitting of uranium and plutonium. It is particularly dangerous because it has a long life, lodges in bone, and can cause cancer. The experts had reason to believe that strontium 90 would be carried all over the world via the stratosphere and would contaminate vegetables and milk.

The AEC study of this problem, exquisitely misnamed "Project Sunshine," was not reassuring. It was hard to estimate how serious the strontium-90 hazard might be, because most of the factors involved were unknown quantities: how widely and how rapidly the radiostrontium would spread over the world, by what avenues (soil, plants, and meat animals) it would reach the human body, how much would be incorporated in the skeleton, what effects it would have there, and so on.

Two things were definitely known: that radioactive material in the bones could be highly damaging (as shown by the tragic case of the radium watch-dial painters), and that the H-bomb test of 1952 had thrown large amounts of strontium 90 into the atmosphere. Plans were already underway for the series of further tests to be held at Bikini in the spring of 1954. These would release many times the amount of fission products that had come from the *Mike* shot, and some of the scientists were concerned about the worldwide fallout that would ensue. But no word of their worries reached the public.

The people of every nation on earth, and most of all the citizens of the nations that were contaminating the atmosphere, have good reason to take a dim view of the iron secrecy that was maintained on the fallout hazard. The hazard raised a major issue of public health, for the radio-active debris would filter into the food supply of most of the world. Surely the Atomic Energy Act of 1946, creating the AEC as a classified enterprise, was never intended to hide such a development from the public. Yet the shibboleth of secrecy, which still enshrouds all nuclear matters, was so strong that not even the uneasy scientists dared to speak up about the danger.

It took a dramatic accident to bring the dimensions of the fallout phenomenon to the world's attention.

On the morning of March 1, 1954, the United States Joint Task Force made ready to fire the powerful H-bomb, *Bravo*, in the Bikini Atoll. The Task Force had taken the pre-caution of clearing all shipping out of a large, rectangular area of the Pacific, extending 70 miles east of the explosion site. This, one may deduce, was done more to keep away un-invited observers than from fears of heavy fallout, for the range of downwind fallout, if it were indeed a serious hazard, would certainly be more than 70 miles. At all events, the ten ships of the Task Force took their stations some 30 miles east of the shot island. The wind was expected to carry the bomb debris northward. To play safe, the Navy had equipped the ships with a system of pipes which would spray a veil of water up from the decks to wash away any downfall of bomb debris.

When the bomb was detonated, the mushroom cloud rose to an altitude of 114,000 feet; then, instead of moving off to the north, it was driven east by a shift of the high-altitude winds. Shortly after the explosion, Geiger counters on the Navy ships began to rattle a warning. Soon the ships were caught in the tenuous but sinister grip of a mantle of radioactive particles falling from the sky. At the order, "Prepare for atomic attack!" all personnel vanished below decks and the ships were "buttoned up," with all ventilators closed off. The spray equipment was turned on; tons and tons of water poured from the decks to sluice the fallout away. The men sweated out the "attack" in tropical heat below decks until the ships had sped away from the shadow of the cloud and technicians in masks and protective clothing had explored the decks with Geiger counters and pronounced them safe.

A Japanese tuna fishing boat named the *Lucky Dragon,* which lay some 90 miles east of the explosion and had somehow escaped the notice of the Task Force scouts, was not so well prepared. The trawler drifted in the lazy swells of the Pacific. The fishing on this voyage had been bad, and the 23 fishermen aboard were waiting doggedly for the tuna to bite. At breakfast time they had been alarmed by a strangely brilliant flash in the sky to the west and by the roll of distant thunder. Now, hours later, there came a still stranger aftermath. The sky misted over in a curious manner, and a whitish-gray dust drifted down. It laid a coat of particles on the deck, crunching underfoot.

The startled crew hauled in its lines and headed for home. Some of the fishermen began to experience radiation sickness. It is difficult to estimate how heavy a dose the crew received, but the symptoms suggest that in some cases it was probably several hundred roentgens. From the pattern of fallout over the general area, as indicated by AEC measurements on certain islands which were finally released in the *Effects* report of 1962, it appears that the *Lucky Dragon* narrowly missed being caught in a lethal zone; had the boat been ten miles south of where it was, probably the entire crew would have been killed by the fallout.

By the time the *Lucky Dragon* reached its home port in Japan, the whole world knew what fallout meant. The full story of this ominous episode has been told in detail, and I will not recount it here. We need to look further, however, into what it disclosed about the *Bravo* bomb.

The great amount of fallout from this bomb was a puzzle. A thermonuclear explosion should not have been so "dirty"; presumably it would emit only a moderate output of fission products from the A-bomb trigger. Yet analysis indicated that about two-thirds of the *Bravo* bomb's 15 megatons of energy had come from uranium fission!

The puzzle was soon solved. When the *Lucky Dragon* arrived in Japan, scientists at the University of Tokyo analyzed the fallout ash that had stuck to its deck. One of the substances in the debris turned out to be an isotope of uranium which is not found in nature—U-237. It happened that the scientist who detected it, Professor Kenjiro Kimura, knew this isotope; he had discovered it in 1939. How was it made? By bombarding U-238 with fast neutrons. U-237 is produced by what physicists call an (n,2n) reaction; that is, the U-238 atom absorbs one neutron and then emits two neutrons.

This meant the bomb must have contained a substantial amount of U-238. That was odd, for no one outside the H-bomb project had thought of ordinary uranium as bomb fuel. But bomb fuel it certainly could be. Struck by very fast neutrons, U-238 might be either fissioned or converted to U-237. The heavy fallout and the presence of traces of U-237 in the fallout led me to the conclusion that the *Bravo* bomb had been loaded with U-238 to augment the explosion.

The H-bomb, then, was in reality a triple-action affair— a fission-fusion-fission bomb. First a fission trigger set off the thermonuclear explosion; this in turn attacked a massive U-238 jacket with a swarm of fast neutrons that caused it to explode. The U-238 jacket actually served three purposes: (1) it kept in neutrons to intensify the explosion, (2) it added to the bomb's power by exploding itself, and (3) it multiplied the supply of neutrons by releasing two neutrons for each one absorbed.

Above all, this "breakthrough" in weaponry made the nuclear bomb not just a one-shot affair but a monstrosity of long-term effects. An attack with such weapons could make a whole nation its target and render the land uninhabitable for a long period. To overkill, the F-F-F bomb added a new dimension—slowkill.

Despite the *Lucky Dragon* incident, the Atomic Energy Commission, then controlled by chairman Lewis L. Strauss, was slow to release information about the fallout. Not until nearly a year afterward did it disclose that the fission debris from the *Bravo* bomb had enveloped some 7,000 square miles of the Pacific in serious to lethal radioactivity. On one deserted island a hundred miles from the explosion a total dose of 3,300 roentgens was recorded within four days.

Even in this report the AEC continued to play down the general significance of fallout. It asserted: "The main radio-activity of a bomb's fallout decreases very rapidly with time —for the most part, within the first hours of the detonation." And Dr. John C. Bugher, the AEC's director of biology and medicine, had told the Industrial Health Conference at its annual meeting in September 1954: "I estimate that the amount of [strontium 90 from bomb tests] now present over the United States would have to be increased by the order of one million times before an increased frequency of bone sarcoma from this cause could be recognized."

The AEC gradually gave ground in its estimates. Within five months after Dr. Bugher's speech it changed his "one million times" to "many thousand times." In 1957 it grudgingly disclosed that radioactivity on the island 100 miles from the *Bravo* shot had persisted for many months after the shot. It also released its report on "Project Sunshine," revealing its concern about strontium 90. Moreover, studies by its biologists made increasingly clear that even the low doses of fallout from bomb testing were likely to have genetic effects upon future generations of mankind.

As testing continued, the hazards from other radioactive fission products besides strontium 90 increased in importance. The contamination of milk by iodine 131 rose to alarming levels in our Midwestern states. Radio-iodine concentrates in the thyroid gland, and it is a special hazard for children. Dr. Russell H. Morgan, chairman of the National Advisory Committee on Radiation, reported that there was "accumulating evidence that radiation delivered to the neck and throat of infants and children may induce cancer of the thyroid gland after the elapse of a number of years."

We cannot get any real conception of the danger, however, by focusing merely on bomb-test fallout. A nuclear war would raise the mortal statistics and the horror to an altogether different level.

The United States Strategic Air Command today probably has the capacity to coat an enemy's soil with radioactivity from more than 10,000 megatons of fission explosions. Let us try to calculate what such an attack would mean. In the regions of heavy attack (that is, those containing the main targets) the deposit of fission products would amount to an average of some three kilotons of explosive per square mile. No one exposed for any length of time in the first days could remain alive. The dose rate in the open one hour after the explosion would be some 6,000 roentgens per hour. By the end of the second day the radiation would fall to 60 roentgens per hour, and by the end of the first week, to 13 roentgens per hour. These are still lethal levels for 24-hour exposure; no one could emerge from a shelter for more than a short time. Even after one month, with the level down to 2.5 roentgens per hour, it would be too dangerous to resume above-ground living. Yet to remain buried for such a period would strain a surviving population beyond endurance. And even when it was safe to emerge, the environment above ground could hardly sustain life. No nation would want to feed its people the food grown on land contaminated by such a fallout. Those who did not sicken and die would live only to propagate a race permanently damaged with a crippling genetic inheritance.

Fallout, in short, adds a unique element to the consequences of war. Even after the explosions stop, men will suffer the slow anger of the ravished atom. Not only the demolished battlegrounds, but much of the planet, will become a hostile environment.

# 6

# *The Missiles*

By 1965 the United States will have a strategic force of more than one thousand ballistic missiles. They will have become our prime instrument of deterrence. Despite the die-hard assertions of Air Force generals that missiles will not replace bombers, it is clear that the bomber's day is waning fast. The bomb-delivery system of the future—the near future—will be missiles.

Civilians are so awed by the unspeakable power of nuclear bombs that they tend to overlook the importance of delivery. Without means of delivery, the military power of the bombs, no matter how immense the stockpile, would be zero. The nuclear warhead, in fact, is only one component of the fantastic weapon that man has now contrived. The vehicle that carries it is fully as terrifying. It is more remarkable in its way, and a great deal more expensive, than the warhead itself.

The rock that Stone-Age man learned to throw accurately at a fleeing or charging animal—or at a two-legged adversary—was the first ballistic missile, and in many ways it paralleled the modern ICBM. It was propelled by chemical energy stored in the man's muscle; it was guided by a coordinated system of eye, brain, and hand; it required a memory-storage and computing device that could correlate distance, velocity, and trajectory. The modern missile is more powerful and in certain respects somewhat more complex. Whereas a man may hurl an eight-ounce rock at a speed of 60 miles per hour to a target within his line of sight, an ICBM must project a thousands-of-times heavier payload at some 16,000 miles per hour to an unseen target thousands of miles away. Among the multitude of factors it must take into account are the rotation of the earth and the variations of the atmosphere along its globe-girdling path.

The first of the breed of modern long-range missiles was Hitler's weapon of vengeance—the V-2. The liquid-fueled Atlas, Titan, and even the mighty Saturn are its direct descendants. V-2 was a single-stage rocket whose engine burned liquid oxygen and alcohol. This fuel mixture was fed through a maze of plumbing into a combustion chamber where it burned to produce a thrust of about 60,000 pounds. That was sufficient to propel a one-ton warhead 200 miles. The V-2's accuracy was not notable; in the bombing of London it often missed its mark by 15 or 20 miles—an imprecision not particularly appreciated by the residents of London and its environs.

Hitler's designers had on the drafting tables a two-stage

rocket with which he hoped to span the Atlantic and bombard the United States. This was a foolish hope: it would have taken his puny Peenemunde project many years to develop a booster powerful enough. Moreover, the missile's accuracy would have been so poor that it would have had small chance of coming close enough to a target to damage it, even with an A-bomb warhead. At best, at such range the missile launchers might have picked a city as a target and considered that they had done well if they hit the state in which it was located.

Shortly after the end of the war, the Pentagon, with the advice and enthusiastic encouragement of the German rocket experts it had brought to the United States, set up a study (Project MX-774) of the possibility of developing a long-range missile to carry the A-bomb. The Pentagon experts finally decided that the prospects looked very bleak. To propel the five-ton A-bomb over a distance of many hundreds of miles would require a huge, multistage rocket of perhaps 500 tons. For development of such a rocket, a whole new technology and a new industry would have to be created. Furthermore, the guidance problem looked extremely formidable. Even the A-warhead called for laying down the missile within two miles of its target, and such accuracy seemed out of the question. I was a scientific adviser to the War Department General Staff at the time, and I recall that many missile experts felt that the best attainable CEP would be 20 miles. CEP ("circular error probability") is a technical term denoting the size of the circle within which 50 per cent of the missiles aimed at a target will fall. A CEP of 20 miles means that 50 per cent will hit within 20 miles of the target and the rest will fall outside that radius.

The United States military planners concluded that the IBM (as it was then called) was too great a gamble, considering the limited defense budget, and on July 8, 1947, the project was cancelled. The Army and its German experts went on making experimental shots with the V-2's captured in Germany and with new, smaller rockets (the Aerobee and the second-stage WAC Corporal), but the big research program was laid aside. The best bet for a nuclear striking force, it was decided, was a fleet of long-range jet bombers.

The stepping up of the arms race after the Soviet explosion of an A-bomb, however, revived the United States missile project. Early in 1951 the Air Force reactivated Project MX-744 and commissioned the General Dynamics Corporation to study the feasibility of an intercontinental ballistic missile. The company's Convair Division in San Diego began to work on the problem, but for some three years it was not pushed very hard.

The successful test of the first thermonuclear device (*Mike*) in the fall of 1952 quickened interest in the missile idea. John von Neumann, whose opinion the Air Force held in high regard, urged that the H-bomb made the development of an ICBM all-important. Trevor Gardner, then Assistant Secretary of the Air Force, decided that the missile program must be speeded up. He persuaded Dr. von Neumann to head an advisory committee with the assignment of assessing the feasibility of an ICBM, drawing up a specific program with a timetable, and outlining an organization for the project.

The von Neumann committee took a fresh look at the problem and came up with a much more optimistic view than the experts had taken in 1947. The committee said that a reliable and reasonably accurate (CEP: five miles) intercontinental missile could be made within five to ten years. It might carry an H-bomb warhead of one or two megatons. While this would be less than one-tenth as powerful as the 24-megaton bomb carried by the B-52 bomber, and the missile's accuracy would not be nearly as good as that of a bomber, at least at first, the missile would have important advantages. Bombers were highly vulnerable to destruction by nuclear weapons, both on their airfields and over the target. The slender ICBM could be sunk in an underground silo for protection, and because of its speed it would be hard to intercept on its way to the target.

The von Neumann group's recommendations gained strong impetus from two developments in 1954. First, the H-bomb was brought into being as a deliverable weapon in the Castle series of tests. Then, radar observations and intelligence reports from behind the Iron Curtain indicated that Soviet scientists were making progress in ballistic-missile rocketry. The Air Force set out to intensify the United States efforts on the basis of the von Neumann recommendations. It created a Western Development Division, under the command of Brigadier General Bernard A. Schriever, to push forward with the design and building of the ICBM on which Convair was working. This was the missile that came to be known as the Atlas.

The specifications for Atlas were selected with great care. The missile had to be large enough to convey a megaton warhead thousands of miles, yet small enough to be housed in an underground silo. Its designers decided upon a two-stage vehicle with three engines, giving a total of 360,000 pounds of thrust. The first stage had the two main boosters, each providing 150,000 pounds of thrust and fueled by liquid oxygen and kerosene. Part of this stage was to be dropped when it burned out, and the missile was to be sent on its course by a second-stage engine like that of the

V-2, giving 60,000 pounds of thrust. In its final version the Atlas weighed 120 tons and measured 85 feet from base to nose tip.

In midyear of 1957 (months before Sputnik), the Air Force successfully launched its first Atlas at Cape Canaveral. The missile was a cumbersome object that took months to prepare for firing and days of final countdown before it could be launched. But it performed its mission, and much better than the von Neumann planners had hoped. Within two years after the first firing the Atlas was hitting within two miles of its target, and by 1960 its programmers looked forward to an accuracy (or CEP) within one mile!

This history puts the missile race in a perspective rather different from the common impression. When the Soviet Union orbited Sputnik I on October 4, 1957—a date the world will long remember as man's first reach into space —the United States missile makers were dismayed by the size of its payload: more than half a ton. The second and third Sputniks were still heavier, Sputnik III carrying a payload of a ton and a half. Including the weight of the booster, the Russian rocket engines in each of these cases must have hurled a total weight of some four tons into space. This probably meant the rockets had a thrust of about 800,000 pounds, far more powerful than that of the Atlas. It did not necessarily mean, however, that the Soviet designers were working at a higher level of refinement in missilry, from a military point of view, than those in the United States.

The Soviet rocketeers seem to have had, from the outset, a different objective. They adopted a brute-force approach, striving for powerful boosters and maximum payloads. It may be that they were looking toward the development of very large A-bombs; at all events, they apparently planned for ICBMs capable of carrying some 10 or 15 tons of warhead. (Sputnik VII *orbited* a weight of 7.1 tons!) By the time they developed their giant boosters, however, the creation of the H-bomb and the improvement of yield-to-weight ratios had reduced the weight of nuclear weapons. Megatons of explosive power could be had without great weight. In a sense, then, the Soviet rockets were oversized as military missiles. If we take the view that Premier Khrushchev decided at that point to capitalize on his giant rockets by impressing the world with spectacular space exploits, it might be said that the Soviet bulldozer approach to the ICBM became the most successful technological "mistake" in history!

We shall see presently how the Soviet missile posture has affected their strategy and ours, but first let us review briefly the growth of the United States missile program.

By 1957, when the first Atlas was launched, the United States was already spending $1 billion a year for research and development on ballistic missiles; today this has become a huge, multibillion-dollar industry. In 1962 the Air Force was reported to have a total of 126 Atlas ICBMs—36 model D, 18 model E, and 72 model F. The F type has an inertial guidance system and is stored underground on a vertical launcher which is protected by massive reinforced concrete doors and is elevated to the surface for firing. Adding up all the costs of the program, I would estimate that the in-hole cost of each Atlas is $40 million.

The Atlas, of course, has been joined by a large family of other missiles. In 1955, before Atlas was built, the Air Force started work on a second ICBM as a "back-up" project in case the Atlas concept should fail. This was the Titan, a liquid-fueled missile designed to carry a warhead of five to ten megatons and to be sited in hardened bases. Titan I is fueled with kerosene and liquid oxygen and has a five-megaton warhead. Fifty-four Titan I's were scheduled for installation at five locations west of the Mississippi. Like Atlas, Titan passed its tests successfully and led to an improved model, Titan II. This stands 110 feet tall, weighs 125 tons, and is powered by an engine system of 430,000 pounds of thrust which burns a mixture of nitrogen tetroxide and hydrazine. Since it does not require liquid oxygen and has its fuel already stored in the engines, it can be fired quickly from its silo. Construction of more than 50 Titan II's has been authorized.

In an era of missile strategy and push-button warfare, the readiness and vulnerability of the missile bases become all-important. How "hard" are the hardened ICBM bases? What does it take to knock them out? Let us consider the arithmetic of missile attack and defense.

The hardened United States bases are designed to withstand a blast overpressure of 100 pounds per square inch. To destroy a silo possessing that resistance, a one-megaton warhead would have to hit within two-thirds of a mile of it, a ten-megaton weapon within 1.4 miles, and a 100-megatonner within about three miles. Obviously the accuracy of the attacking missiles is much more important than their size. Given an accurate guidance system, it would be a poor investment to use a 100-megaton warhead (assuming that this could be carried by an ICBM). At least two 100-megatonners would have to be launched against a target, since no launching could be counted on for 100 per cent reliability. That would be an extravagant waste of nuclear explosive and giant rocket engines if half a dozen ten-megatonners could do the job. Thus the 100-megaton bomb is not really a military weapon but a weapon of national destruction. We will confine our analysis, then, to warheads of practical military size—say one megaton and ten megatons. Taking the case of the one-megaton warhead first, if the missile's CEP (circular error probability) is two miles, then about 40 missiles will have to be fired at a single silo target to give a 90 per cent probability of knocking it out; if the CEP is one mile, it will still take about ten missiles to be reasonably sure of killing the ICBM in its silo. With a ten-megaton warhead, on the other hand, ten to twelve missiles will do if the CEP is two miles, and three will be sufficient if it is one mile. Thus, with an accuracy within one mile and ten-megaton warheads, an enemy could knock out our hardened Atlas and Titan bases with a few hundred ICBMs.

In the process, he would also spread destruction and fallout over a large portion of the United States, including many large cities—among them St. Louis, Tucson, Kansas City, Wichita, Omaha, Denver, Spokane, and Los Angeles. The city of Tucson, for example, is ringed with 18 hardened Titan bases. If the enemy launched a minimum of two ten-megaton warheads against each of those silos, a total of some 360 megatons would fall in the vicinity of that city. The radioactive fallout from such an attack would be so heavy that, according to an estimate by James E. McDonald, professor of atmospheric physics at the University of Arizona, the area would be lethal to human life for at least three months.

Despite objections, the Air Force refused to change the location of its missile bases, although many of them were upwind of populated areas. At civil-defense hearings of Chet Holifield's House subcommittee in 1960, I pointed out that the proposed bases would become magnets attracting nuclear fire to American cities in the event of war. Rep-

73

resentative Holifield later attacked the Air Force's policy on location of its bases as a "completely inexcusable and . . . reprehensible" mistake. The Defense Department, however, defended its position. It stated at a Congressional hearing: "While the Air Force realized the potential danger to the civilian population in proximity to missile bases, this consideration was not determining [sic!] in the location of these bases."

General Thomas D. White, Chief of Staff for the Air Force, later sought to justify its position: "I think one should not minimize the effects of fallout, but I believe that in an atomic war fallout is inevitable no matter what we do. We have to have these missile bases, and we endeavor to put them, where possible, in unpopulated areas, but sometimes inevitably they do fall to the west [*i.e.*, upwind]. If we put them in the eastern part of the United States as a general rule, although we do have some there for targeting reasons, we would subject the most heavily populated area of this country to possible needless attack. I cannot conceive of an all-out atomic war in which cities as well as bases are not going to be destroyed and subject to fallout."

With this last prediction there can be no dispute. There is an alternative, however, to placing missile bases near the population, and the Defense Department, for reasons of its own, was already developing that alternative: namely, creating a nuclear striking force which would be mounted on moving bases at sea (*i.e.*, submarines) rather than at fixed land bases. The reason was not primarily protection of the population but the need to make the striking force less vulnerable to knock-out by an enemy.

In 1956 the Navy had set up a Special Projects Office and assigned Rear Admiral William F. Raborn to lead it in the development of a solid-fuel rocket which could be launched from a submarine. Within two years this missile, named Polaris, and a program for arming a fleet of nuclear-powered submarines with it were well underway. The Navy thus came into competition with the Air Force in the role of providing the strategic force for deterrence against attack. But it had an appealing slogan which disarmed overt opposition in the Pentagon or in Congress:

*Move deterrence out to sea,*
*Where real estate is free,*
*And where it's far away from me.*

In effect, the Polaris submarine is the first stage of a missile. Powered by nuclear engines which can take it on very long journeys under water, it roams the world's oceans in concealment and can fire its missiles from within comparatively short range of the enemy. Because it does not need to be fired as far as an ICBM, the Polaris rocket can be much smaller. The missile is 26 feet long. It is fitted with a 600-pound warhead yielding nearly two-thirds of a megaton of explosive power—more than 30 times that of the Hiroshima bomb.

The submarine locker in which the Polaris is housed first pops the missile up out of the water by compressed air. The rocket then is ignited, and its two stages throw the warhead into a ballistic trajectory. An inertial guidance system of gyroscopes and accelerometers, coupled to computers, keeps the missile on course during the powered part of its flight; the computers signal the cut-off of the second-stage engine and the release of the warhead at the proper time. For accurate aiming at the target, it is essential that the submarine know its precise position with respect to the target when the Polaris is released. In the broad ocean, this is a

75

very tricky problem. It was solved by the development of an elaborate device called SINS (ship's inertial navigation system) which automatically tells the submarine's exact position on the globe at all times. The Polaris submarine carries three of these devices.

Each submarine has 16 Polaris missiles, adding up to a total fire power of about ten megatons. The range of the missile started at 1,200 to 1,500 miles but has been extended to 2,500 miles. The Navy has authorized construction of 41 Polaris submarines, carrying a total of 656 missiles. Counting the cost of the submarines (about $110 million apiece), each Polaris missile will represent an investment of more than $10 million—about one-fourth the cost of an Atlas or a Titan in its hardened silo.

The Air Force, not to be outdone, also set out to acquire a "cheap," solid-fuel, instant-firing missile like the Polaris. The weapon it developed was a three-stage ICBM called the Minuteman, capable of carrying a warhead of about the same size as the Polaris for a distance of some 6,000 miles. The Minuteman is a slim, 54-foot projectile, shaped like a bullet but weighing 65,000 pounds. It fits into a concrete silo some 80 feet deep and only ten feet in diameter. A reinforced-concrete sliding door four feet thick covers its hole. The missile can be readied for firing from its silo within 30 seconds. It is a case of one silo, one shot—for the exhaust gases destroy the launcher so that the silo cannot be used again. Surrounded by three acres of ground enclosed with barbed-wire fencing, the Minuteman has no attendants at its silo; it is fired by remote control by officers in underground shelters some distance away. The nuclear warhead cannot explode in its silo, because the switch that arms it for firing is not turned on until after the missile has been launched.

A total of 800 Minutemen has been authorized. In squadrons of 50 and flights of ten, they will be based at Air Force centers in Montana, North and South Dakota, Missouri, and other central states.

What has the Soviet Union been doing, meanwhile, in missilry? Whatever information the United States may have on this vital question is known only to our intelligence agencies. But some reasonable guesses can be made. The Russians' reaction to our U-2 flights over their country provides illuminating clues.

The giant Soviet rockets probably could carry warheads of 20 megatons or more. Yet the very size of the huge boosters is their Achilles heel. One high United States official has said: "Russia does not bother to harden—that is, to put her ICBMs under the ground. Some of their launching pads look like so many huge asparagus beds." The monstrous missiles would be most difficult to conceal or bury in hardened silos. They would be easy targets for destruction. As long as the U.S.S.R. was able to conceal its rocket activities and its missile sites behind the Iron Curtain, it was not urgently concerned about this problem. But our U-2 overflights destroyed that security. It is now generally known that the U-2s made revealing photographs of the Soviet rocket locations. As a result, the Soviet planners no doubt felt that they must speed up the development of less vulnerable ICBMs.

On this line of reasoning, it becomes easier to understand why Premier Khrushchev broke the moratorium and resumed the testing of nuclear weapons in the fall of 1961. His multimegaton explosions in that series of tests were stunts for psychological and political purposes, but along with these the Soviet tested many smaller weapons. Professor Hans Bethe told a Congressional committee that many of them were "in the range from one to five megatons." What could this mean? It suggests that in all likelihood the Soviet weaponeers were testing more efficient new bombs as warheads for modest-sized ICBMs that could be placed in hardened and concealed silos. The Soviet Union, then, must have its own counterparts of the Minuteman, the Polaris, the Titan, and so on.

Without doubt the intercontinental ballistic missiles of the nuclear powers will advance rapidly in power, ease of firing, and accuracy. By 1965 their accuracy is expected to be one mile or less—good enough to pinpoint any target. They are already highly automatic—especially the Minuteman— and capable of being fired in salvos. They compress the time-scale of war to a point that allows no time for hesitation or deliberate thought and opens the door wide to global destruction by accident. The era of push-button warfare is already here.

Tartaglia, the great ballistics expert of the sixteenth century, had a guilty premonition of the shape of things to come. In the preface to his *The Art of Projecting Bombs*, he wrote:

"One day meditating to myself, it seemed to me that it was a thing blameworthy, shameful, and barbarous, worthy of severe punishment before God and man, to wish to bring to perfection an art damageable to one's neighbor and destruction to the human race. . . ."

# 7

# *The Paradoxes*
# *of Deterrence*

It was Sir Winston Churchill who, in his customary style, first enunciated in vivid terms the policy of building up nuclear weapons to deter aggression and prevent war. In 1948 he declared at the annual conference of the British Conservative Party that if the United States were to consent to destroy its stocks of atomic bombs, "they would be guilty of murdering human freedom and committing suicide themselves." Later, after the Soviet Union also had atomic bombs, Churchill coined the phrase "peace through mutual terror." He predicted that, "by a process of sublime irony," the world would reach a stage "where safety will be the sturdy child of terror, and survival the twin brother of annihilation."

Sir Winston's sentiments were echoed by American spokesmen, for nuclear deterrence did become the foundation of United States policy. Air Force Secretary Thomas K. Finletter, speaking at the West Point commencement exercises in 1953, said that nuclear power represented a "new strategic concept—a concept of a deterrent force." The United States and the U.S.S.R., he observed, "now have weapons so devastating in their nature that it is highly likely that both sides will destroy themselves, or at least the essence of their civilization, if they should ever go into all-out conflict."

President Eisenhower made the United States policy explicit in his address to the United Nations on December 8, 1953: "Should . . . an atomic attack be launched against the United States, our reactions would be swift and resolute." He added that the American nuclear arsenal "could inflict terrible losses upon an aggressor" and lay waste its land.

Such phrases, however, are only the outline of a policy. What does deterrence mean in concrete terms? In 1954 Secretary of State John Foster Dulles set forth what it meant, as the Executive Branch then saw it, in his famous speech describing the policy of "massive, instant retaliation." Addressing the Council on Foreign Relations, Mr. Dulles said:

". . . before military planning could be changed, the President and his advisers, as represented by the National Security Council, had to take some basic policy decisions. This has been done. The basic decision was to depend primarily upon a great capacity to retaliate, instantly, by means and at places of our choosing."

The late Secretary went on to add that "massive" retaliation would mean "placing more reliance on deterrent power and less dependence on local defense power."

Mr. Dulles may have supposed that his statement was simple and clear enough, but it evoked a massive, instant reaction and a host of alarming questions. For one thing, the Pentagon, its friends in Congress, and industry immediately took alarm at the proposed cuts in spending for conventional arms (such as tanks, etc.). Far more disquieting, however, was the retaliation formula itself. Did it mean that in the event of another Korea the United States would retaliate massively and directly against China or the Soviet Union?

Secretary Dulles hastened to climb back from that limb. Flying back to the United States from a mission to Berlin, he wrote a "more polished restatement" of his views. Massive retaliation, he said, "does not mean turning every local war into a world war. It does not mean that if there is a Communist attack somewhere in Asia, atom or hydrogen bombs will necessarily be dropped on the great industries of China or Russia." The Secretary amplified his views further in a press conference:

> "The question of the circumstances under which you retaliate, where you retaliate, how quickly you retaliate is a matter which has to be dealt with in the light of the facts of each particular case. One thing I want to make clear beyond possibility of doubt is that I don't believe you should tell the enemy in advance just where, how, and when you plan to retaliate. The whole essence of the program is that the action should be an action of our choosing and he is not to know in advance what it is, and that uncertainty on his part is a key to the success of the policy."

By "clarifying" the policy in such detail, Mr. Dulles laid himself open to many embarrassing questions. His "keep 'em guessing" strategy was a hodge-podge of contradictions.

Any effective system of deterrence by the threat of pun-

81

ishment must rest upon a clear and specific understanding of exactly what acts will be punished, and under what circumstances and to what degree they will be penalized. Mr. Dulles compared the deterrence policy to a "community security system" prepared to "punish any who break in and steal." But in a community security system there is an established code of forbidden acts, and courts impose on those found guilty certain advertised penalties fitted to the crime.

Precisely what kind of aggression would be met with massive retaliation? For the case of a nuclear attack by the Soviet Union upon the United States, Mr. Dulles' coy talk of not letting the enemy know in advance just where, when, and how the United States would retaliate made no sense; retaliation would be an inevitable, swift reflex. What about lesser aggressions? The Dulles policy conceded that not *every* local war would be turned into a world war and that bombs would not *necessarily* be dropped on China or Russia. This implied that *some* local wars might be turned into world war. What kinds, and how would aggression be defined or recognized? For such contingencies the policy of massive retaliation—an all-or-nothing policy—was at once extremely dangerous and ludicrous. On one hand, it would keep the United States continually on the brink of possible disaster. On the other, it might turn into a monumental bluff which would progressively diminish the influence and prestige of the United States in the world.

We cannot dismiss Secretary Dulles' inconsistencies as mere brainstorms of a naïve man. The fact is that his attempts at explanation brought into sharp relief the inherent contradictions of the massive-retaliation policy. Those contradictions have not been resolved with the passage of time and the refinement of strategy; if anything, they have been intensified. The multimegaton bomb and the half-hour intercontinental missile—the logical results of the massive-retaliation philosophy—have pushed the concept to its ultimate absurdity. In the days of the leisurely bomber, governments might perhaps have deliberated on where, when, and how to retaliate, but the luxury of deliberate decision has now been abolished. Nor would the United States have time to consult with its allies. "Instant" today means instant, and military action takes on the character of pure reflex. Brinkmanship has ceased to be a cute figure of speech.

Few of the questions I have discussed were examined seriously at the time Dulles enunciated the massive-retaliation policy. One of them is especially interesting and has grown in significance since then. This is Dulles' reference to attacking the enemy at "places of our choosing." If that means targets to be attacked in the Soviet Union, it becomes interesting to reflect on the fact that in 1954 our intelligence services knew very little about Soviet target locations (other than cities). In all likelihood the retaliation concept was primarily responsible for our proceeding to develop the U-2 for high-altitude reconnaissance.

In 1954 the Air Force authorized funds for it, and the Lockheed Aircraft Corporation built the plane. Lockheed had been working on a successor to the F-104 jet fighter to fly at high altitudes, and it was able to produce the U-2 in short order. In 1956 it turned over a few completed planes to a joint intelligence enterprise of the Air Force and the Atomic Energy Commission (called AFOAT-1). The intelligence group put them to work collecting air samples at high altitude from Soviet nuclear tests and also for reconnaissance overflights within the Soviet Union.

The flights were highly successful. Defense Secretary Thomas S. Gates, Jr. later reported to Congress: ". . . from these flights we got information on airfields, aircraft, missiles, missile testing and training, special weapons storage, submarine production, atomic production and aircraft deployment, and things like these. . . . These results were considered in formulating our military programs."

The U.S.S.R. could hardly be blamed for taking an alarmed view of this and wondering just what "our military programs" might be. Some of the installations mentioned would seem to be more appropriate targets for a first-strike attack than for a retaliatory blow. It is no wonder that Premier Khrushchev reacted so violently to the U-2 business and seized the opportunity to make propaganda capital of President Eisenhower's acknowledgement of personal responsibility for the flights. An announced policy of massive retaliation is well calculated to produce maximum insecurity and suspicion, for only a razor's edge separates this threat from the threat of massive anticipatory attack.

Insofar as local wars (*i.e.*, minor aggressions) were concerned, the policy of massive retaliation eventually fell of its own weight. Neither civilians nor the military could live with the awesome thought that any small war might explode into a world nuclear conflict. Deterrence-minded thinkers began to speculate on finding a way to have one's cake and eat it too: that is, to use nuclear weapons to discourage aggression without engulfing whole nations.

The Council on Foreign Relations undertook to study the problems "of foreign policy in the nuclear age," and a group of 33 experts under the chairmanship of Gordon Dean devoted a year and a half to this study. In 1957 the study director, Dr. Henry Kissinger, expounded its conclusions in a book titled *Nuclear Weapons and Foreign Policy*. The essence of this work was a doctrine of limited nuclear warfare, using tactical nuclear weapons and confining them to the battlefield.

How could their use be confined? Dr. Kissinger proposed a code of nuclear conduct—a kind of Marquis of Queensberry Rules—to which the contestants would pledge themselves. It would be designed to prevent military engagements from escalating to a general conflagration.

The idea of reducing nuclear weapons to strictly military implements in the old-fashioned sense (pre-World War II) looked attractive—to civilians if not to the military. Dr. Kissinger's prescription became popular in Government circles. Secretary Dulles embraced it, backing down somewhat from his massive-retaliation doctrine. Pointing out that the AEC had tested small nuclear weapons which confined their effects to particular targets, he declared that "it may be possible to defend countries by nuclear weapons so mobile, or so placed, as to make military invasion with conventional forces a hazardous attempt."

Professor Edward Teller went further: he foresaw a prospect of fighting limited nuclear wars "in a humane way." This would be accomplished by developing "clean" H-bombs that produced little radioactive fallout. In company with other scientists and Chairman Strauss of the AEC, Teller went to the White House to explain the technicalities of this concept to President Eisenhower. The President later told newsmen: "They say, 'Give us four or five years to test each step of our development and we will produce an absolutely clean bomb.'" To date, the clean bomb has not yet been produced, and physical theory suggests no practical way in which it could be.

The concept of limited nuclear war is even harder to work out. It is almost like asking for a return to the age of chivalry, when combatants fought only on weekdays and carefully avoided engaging towns in their combat. Picture the confrontation of two armies armed with tactical weapons. Their weapons include a wide variety of sizes and ranges. To use the names of those possessed by the United States Army, there are Davy Crockett (the bazooka missile), Long John (range: ten miles), Corporal and Sergeant (75 miles), and Pershing (500 miles). The contestants open fire with their short-range missiles and seek to confine the area of the battle, but how long will the gentlemen's agreement be respected? If its front-line troops are being clobbered, will either side refrain from throwing in supporting fire from the longer-range missile launchers in the rear? Will the other side then refrain from releasing its heaviest possible fire against those launchers, whether they are ten, 75, or 500 miles away?

Battles are still fought by men, and in the heat of battle their behavior is not altogether predictable or subject to rigid control. How will they act in the utter confusion of a nuclear engagement, with whole battalions wiped out at a blow, communications destroyed, and officers in the dark about how the battle is going? What sort of chain of command can be established? Who will have the ultimate say on what weapons are fired? Above all, how will the battle be ended? Will either side accept defeat, so long as it still has powerful weapons that can be thrown into the balance, limited war or no limited war? To suggest that a nuclear conflict could be disciplined or restrained from expanding is indeed an armchair exercise.

The great debate on the doctrine of limited nuclear war came to a predictable conclusion. Aside from Dr. Teller and a few other ardent champions of tactical nuclear weapons, most of the doctrine's advocates ceased to clamor for it. Even its chief exponent, Dr. Kissinger, reconsidered. In an article setting forth "A Reappraisal" of his theory in 1961, he changed his mind about the feasibility of keeping a nuclear war limited.

The question of limiting nuclear war becomes even more acute when we turn to the problem of deterring a major aggression—not a peripheral engagement but a direct attack on our own country or our allies. What form of retaliation would be most effective for discouraging such an attack? In blunt terms, the issue can be stated this way: should the deterrent be based on destroying the aggressor's country (his cities, his industry, and his land) or on destroying only his means of continuing and finishing the war (his missiles, his bases, his whole arsenal of weapons)? The theory of this second alternative is that an aggressor will never launch an attack if he has no chance of prevailing.

In mid-1962 the Kennedy Administration announced that the United States had chosen the second strategy. In a commencement address at the University of Michigan, Secretary of Defense Robert S. McNamara said:

> "The United States has come to the conclusion that, to the extent feasible, basic military strategy in a possible general nuclear war should be approached in much the same way that more conventional military operations have been regarded in the past. That is to say, principal military objectives, in the event of a nuclear war stemming from a major attack on the alliance [i.e., NATO], should be the destruction of the enemy's military forces, not of his civilian population.
>
> "The very strength and nature of the alliance forces make it possible for us to retain, even in the face of a massive surprise attack, sufficient reserve striking power to destroy an enemy society if driven to it. In other words, we are giving a possible opponent the strongest imaginable incentive to refrain from striking our own cities."

87

This version of limited nuclear war, unfortunately, arouses as much skepticism as did Kissinger's. Soviet leaders have steadily maintained that any nuclear war would bring total destruction. Their position was restated, after Mr. Mc-Namara's speech, by Soviet Defense Minister Rodion Malinovsky: "A future war will lead to the deaths of millions of people and will ruin the main centers of civilization." And many United States military men likewise believe that nuclear war cannot be restricted.

Curiously, the issue has been raised in its sharpest form within the United States military services, as a result of the Navy's "intrusion" into the Air Force's role as the nation's strategic defender. Air Force spokesmen have maintained that their mission is primarily the destruction of military targets, whereas the Navy's Polaris striking force would be aimed indiscriminately at large centers such as cities. General Thomas S. Power, commander-in-chief of the Strategic Air Command, defined SAC's mission as "retaliatory attacks designed to destroy the war-making capacity of an aggressor to the point where he would no longer have the will nor the capability to wage war." Lieutenant General James E. Briggs spelled out the SAC philosophy:

> "There are those who believe deterrence to be the threat of indiscriminate bombings. They say that an enemy would not dare to attack if we possess ample power to retaliate by destroying his major cities. The advocates of this minimum deterrence seem to disregard the need for military strength sufficient to defeat any enemy.
>
> "In the final analysis, deterrence exists in the mind of the potential enemy. . . . We cannot afford to asume that limited [!] actions, such as bombing key cities [sic!], would be so frightening to him that he would not wage war. . . . We must have the ability to selectively and decisively destroy [his]

military forces. . . . We must have forces that can prevail, if we would deter."

Here, restated for the nuclear age, was the time-honored military point of view. Unless military force could "defeat" the enemy, could "prevail"—with the implication that the United States would suffer less damage than the enemy—military strategy could have no justification. Never in history, however, has military policy been so tortured with self-doubts and inconsistencies. In a seminar on strategy held at the National War College in 1959, Allen W. Dulles, director of the Central Intelligence Agency, observed dryly: "The theory that either of the great nuclear powers could destroy the other without the attacker himself being devastated is not, I believe, subscribed to on either side of the Iron Curtain."

The Defense Department's budget for fiscal 1963 carried out the new strategy of concentrating on weapons capable of destroying the enemy's military power. In brisk and businesslike fashion, Secretary McNamara explained the program to Congress at the budgetary hearings.

He planned a three-step analysis of the problem to work out the basis for designing an effective deterrent apparatus. The three tasks were to find out: (1) the number, types, and locations of the targets to be destroyed, (2) the number and power of the weapons that would have to be delivered to destroy them, and (3) the best means of delivering these weapons.

About 100 officers and civilians were assigned to these jobs. For the first task the Joint Chiefs of Staff set up a Joint Target Evaluation Group. It was to prepare a "National Strategic Target List." This was no small assignment. To begin with, the group would need to identify all the possible military targets in the Soviet Union and specify their exact locations. With U-2 flights abandoned, other devices for collecting the intelligence would have to be found. Presumably they would include photography from space satellites. Then the group would have to evaluate the importance of each target and its worth to the Kremlin. One wonders how defense specialists in Washington can simulate the mental processes of the men in Moscow. Selection of the targets must involve a complex calculus of strategic thinking, military technology, ideology, economics, sociology, and psychology. For example, what value is to be placed on plants for production of nuclear weapons? To many strategists (even in Washington) these look like high-priority targets. But in the time-scale of missile war, bombing such plants would be an act of futility. The war would be fought with weapons in being; any weapons produced after the first salvos would be too late.

Steps 2 and 3 in Secretary McNamara's program were to culminate in a "Single Integrated Operational Plan"— a detailed schedule of operations designed to destroy the targets on the selected list. Mr. McNamara made a five-part breakdown of the delivery problem; it would entail a comparative study of each vehicle's payload capacity, its ability to penetrate enemy defenses, its accuracy, its launching reliability, and its cost.

Summing up his admirably tidy approach to the deterrence problem, the Secretary remarked: "In contrast to most other military requirements, the requirement for strategic retaliatory forces lends itself rather well to reasonably precise calculation."

If the problem is merely to compute what forces are needed to destroy a given target system, this is certainly true. But unfortunately the real equation is full of unknown and incalculable variables. Faulty intelligence may give a very wrong assessment of the targets. Technological innovation changes the variables from year to year, almost from month to month. An improvement in the accuracy of the enemy's first strike, for example, may prevent the retaliatory force from ever being launched.

There are also more imponderable factors which no analysis by computer can evaluate. When Secretary McNamara was asked how he had decided upon the relative numbers (the "mix") of Minuteman and Polaris missiles he requested in his budget, he replied that the factors taken into account were the invulnerability and effectiveness of the striking forces and their relative costs. Apparently no weight was given to broader security factors, such as whether the missile sites would draw attack upon the United States heartland, whether the retaliatory force could bide its time and make sure a supposed attack was not a false alarm before it fired (as Polaris submarines could), or whether one weapon or the other was likely to become obsolete in a short time. I cite these questions only to illustrate that every weapon decision involves grave consequences for national security which are not subject to "precise calculation."

The policy of deterrence has now been in operation for more than a decade. It cannot be said to have failed, though it has not exactly stopped Communist aggression dead in its tracks. Many believe that the policy has demonstrated its power to prevent nuclear war. The real test of deterrence, however, is the shape of the world it has created—and the outlook ahead. Though the purpose of the policy was to stabilize a touchy, hostility-ridden world, it has, if anything, had the opposite effect. It has generated an endless arms race and created increasingly dangerous forces of instability.

Winston Churchill, the early champion of deterrence, acknowledged that it could not guarantee peace. "The deterrent," he admitted, "does not cover the case of lunatics or dictators in the mood of Hitler when he found himself in his final dugout." The world has been spared, so far, the misfortune of a lunatic coming into control of the push-button. But—what is more terrifying—it has been delivered into the hands of computers. The pregnant phrases of our time are "first strike" and "second strike." In the programs of the computers, and in the scale of time, the two acts are coming closer and closer together, and the time may soon come when, given a situation of extreme tension, attack and retaliation will be indistinguishable. The first strike and the second strike will be practically simultaneous, and any historians who survive to tell the tale may be unable to decide who started the war that destroyed civilization.

# 8

## *The Game of Nuclear War*

As a boy, Karl von Clausewitz liked to roam the countryside fighting hypothetical battles. Here was a hill to be occupied as a strong point, there a stream to be crossed, here a culvert from which one could outflank and surprise the enemy. Such were the war games of the past, as played by boys and generals alike. The modern game of war is imcomparably more sophisticated. It is played by mathematicians feeding complex data into electronic computers, and by analytic statisticians perusing charts in "think factories." There is no place for brilliant maneuvers or deeds of heroism. Even the daring warplane flier of recent vintage has been reduced from soaring into the "wild blue yonder" to sitting prosaically before an underground console of dials and buttons.

The game of imaginary war with the U.S.S.R. is being played unflaggingly by many groups of experts in the United States, such as the RAND Corporation (financed by the Air Force), the Pentagon's Defense Atomic Support Agency, and committees of scientists in universities and research institutes. They have produced a voluminous literature of reports, estimates, forecasts, plans, and programs dealing with various aspects of a possible United States-Soviet war. Most of their conclusions, of course, are classified secret. But enough has emerged in reports to Congress and technical journals to show the trends of their thinking.

In these games extensive use has been made of "operations research" and John von Neumann's "game theory." Operations research, developed during World War II to solve such problems as getting United States convoys across the Atlantic with a minimum of losses to German submarines, is a mathematical technique well suited to dealing with missile warfare. Game theory also is a technique of mathematical analysis; it sets up models to explore the results of various strategies and counter-strategies that may be employed by the contestants in a game.

Let us try to imagine a two-player nuclear game between the United States and the Soviet Union, each armed with the power to destroy and each mortally fearful of the other. Tension, let us say, has almost reached the breaking point, and both sides are weighing the costs of attack and retaliation.

As in any game, whether chess or war, we must assume that the opponent will act in a rational manner—that is, he will consider the consequences of his moves. This means we must try to read his mind, which is to say, we must estimate what price he is willing to pay for an attack launched to defeat us. We are prepared to launch a devastating retalia-

tory attack upon the known resources of the Soviet Union
—its military bases, its 160 major cities (over 100,000 in
population), its industry, its transportation system (85 per
cent railroad), and so forth. Just how much of all this our
counter-attack would destroy is an open question, but let
us say that the Kremlin estimates, as a rough index, that
our retaliatory strike would kill 50 million of the Soviet
Union's population and inflict corresponding destruction
on the country. Would it be willing to pay that price? Would
such a prospective loss deter it from attacking us?

The truth is that we cannot know, and perhaps not
even the Kremlin knows. Some strategists of the United
States Air Force contend that Soviet leaders *would* pay the
price. They recall that the Soviet Union suffered 25 million
casualties in World War II and still fought on—and emerged
as a major power after the war though 40 per cent of its
industrial plant had been destroyed. This is not, however,
a valid basis for judging the effects of a nuclear strike, which
would not be drawn out but would fall with shocking impact
on the whole nation. Moreover, the Soviet decision as to
whether to attack and pay the price would be a coldly calculated one, not a desperate continuation of a struggle for
survival, as it was in World War II. Yet we cannot be certain that the Soviet strategists are not prepared to pay the
price, for they do not publish their analyses and we don't
hear from their Edward Tellers and Herman Kahns.

Now let us consider the game from our side of the table.
Some of our mathematical analysts have become fascinated
with the results of their calculus. Their computers tell them
that, under certain circumstances, we could score a "win" in
a nuclear war. Unhappily, the computer arrives at this result
only because it has no feelings: it grinds out answers with
complete unconcern. It cares not whether the print-out reads

ten million killed or 100 million killed. If Country A loses 30 million dead and 27 per cent of its economy, whereas Country B has 90 million dead and 68 per cent of its economy destroyed, the computer pronounces Country A the winner. One wonders how much consolation that would be to Country A.

Our Defense Department makes the assumption that the enemy's first strike would not knock us out of combat—that we would get up off the floor and fight back. On that assumption, it becomes necessary to find out what we have left to fight with. The gladiator must know: "How badly am I hurt? What strength can I muster?"

To provide this information, in the event of a nuclear attack, the Defense Department has created a nationwide system of automatic sensing devices to measure the power of the attack. Called NUDETS (nuclear detection system), the network includes seismic devices, radiation detectors, and optical instruments, located at strategic points within the United States. They are designed to tell the size, location, and altitude of each nuclear explosion. The sensors would transmit all the data to a chain of computers, which would interpret the information and pass it on to damage assessors at the National Resources Evaluation Center (sometimes called the "what's left department"). To aid in the assessment, the Government has set up a program called Jumbo II. Here, stored on magnetic memory drums, is a collection of information on each of 45,000 divisions of the United States—the density of population in the area, the nature of its housing, its amount of shelter, industrial products, critical resources, and so on. Thus the program will be able to make a quick calculation of the probable damage and casualties in each area from blasts, heat, and fallout—

even before the fallout falls to earth. Supplementing this program, surveys will be made by aircraft and other means to get a total picture of the nation's wounds.

We do not need to wait for the attack, however, to know what might be in store. The experts have already composed a rather detailed picture of the probable effects of a nuclear strike upon the United States. One of their studies emerged from secrecy and was published in the journal *Operations Research*. It describes the fallout punishment to be expected from nuclear attacks; its title is "The Distribution and Effects of Fallout in Large Nuclear-Weapon Campaigns."

The report explains that the formulas used by the authors to estimate the fallout effects were based on information from the RAND Corporation. It goes on to say: "A method of optimally distributing weapons among large areas in order to maximize radiation casualties is deduced on the basis of the formulas, and curves are exhibited expressing the casualties produced as a function of total yield delivered."

Only in the cold detachment of the laboratory and the jargon of expertise is it possible to speak of "optimally distributing weapons . . . to maximize radiation casualties."

The authors' highly mathematical analysis is couched in Greek symbols and complex formulas, but one does not have to be a mathematician or a weapons expert to understand their "curves." These curves (*see following page*) tell a story of life and death for the populations of the United States and the Soviet Union in a nuclear war. They plot the proportion of the population that would die from fallout radiation within 60 days (60 days "response") after megaton attacks of various severities. A 50,000-megaton attack would kill virtually the entire population of the United States or the U.S.S.R., regardless of how it was distributed over the

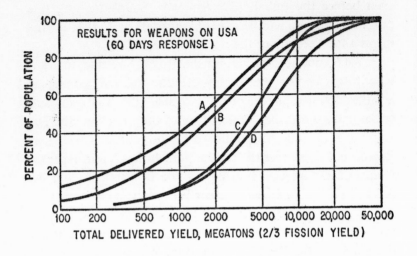

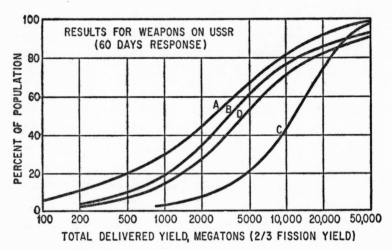

*These charts show the estimated percentages of deaths in an "unprepared" population that would result from nuclear attacks of various weights. The four curves represent fallout deaths from four different bombing doctrines: (A) distributing the warheads over the country in a pattern designed to "maximize" killing of the population; (B) distributing them according to population density; (C) distributing them uniformly over the country; (D) concentrating them on air bases. The upper chart describes the estimated results of such attacks on the United States, and the lower one on the Soviet Union.*

country; even a 10,000-megaton strike would leave comparatively few survivors.

The authors refine their analysis to show how variations in the pattern of attack on each country would affect the number of fallout casualties. The highest curve represents the percentage of kill if the bombs and missiles were so distributed as to "maximize deaths in the unprepared population"—in other words, kill off people as efficiently as possible. Here an attack of only 500 megatons (50 ten-megaton bombs) would kill 30 per cent of our population, and 5,000 megatons (500 such bombs) would kill 80 per cent. The lowest curve shows how many in the nation would die from fallout if the Soviet warheads were aimed only at SAC bases. A 1,000-megaton attack would kill 10 per cent of the population; a 5,000-megaton attack, about 50 per cent. The two middle curves represent the toll of life if the bombs were distributed according to population density or uniformly over the country; these are not the most efficient patterns for killing people.

The curves for the Soviet Union tell much the same story as for the United States, except that in most attacks the death toll would be somewhat lower, because of the larger area of the country and the wider dispersion of its population.

The analysts point out that the figures they have given are not the total toll, for they do not take into account longer-term radiation casualties (after 60 days) from "such delayed effects as the disorganization of society, extinction of livestock, genetic damage, and the slow development of radiation poisoning from the ingestion of radioactive materials."

Scientists who deal with nuclear war games and casualty estimates tend to develop a brittle, formalized language which shields them from the flesh-and-blood impact of their calculations. "Population response" is a protective euphemism for slaughter, and "30 per cent mortality" or "55 megadeaths" does not sound as bad as 55 million Americans dead. (In military circles, deaths from fallout are referred to as "bonus kills.") Amusing as the dehumanized terminology may be, it is not a mere artifact of trivial significance. It would be interesting, perhaps vital, to find out whether the clinical terminology plays a part in hardening the minds of those who are deciding in secret councils what price the United States would pay to "win" a nuclear war.

The most detailed analysis of this subject that has been published was a report by the Joint Committee on Atomic Energy on its hearings in 1959 on "Biological and Environmental Effects of Nuclear War." It was assumed that 224 targets in the United States, 71 of them cities, were hit by 263 bombs totaling 1,446 megatons. The toll from this hypothetical attack was calculated to be 42 million dead and 17 million injured. Fallout accounted for more than half of the deaths.

After adding up the kills and the losses, the players of the game of nuclear war must face up to the aftermath of the war. For unless the "winner" can bind up his wounds, restore his economy, and resume human life, he is no better off than the loser.

How much study our Government has given to the recovery problem is unknown; no authoritative analysis has been published. Some personal views have been offered; I will cite three individual opinions which illustrate the range of thinking on the question.

The most optimistic is Dr. Teller's. In his book titled *The Legacy of Hiroshima,* Teller says:

"Much of the strength of our industrial society, fortunately, is not in our industrial plant. Our factories are expendable. Our strength is in our know-how and in our organization. Our gross national product . . . now is more than 500 billion dollars a year. But the total value of everything that exists in this country —all the houses, clothes, food, factories, minerals, farms, services, cars, everything that can be bought or sold—is only about 1,500 billion dollars. Everything we have, in other words, could be produced by our present industrial complex in only about three years. . . .

"This also means that survivors of an all-out nuclear attack, given food and a bare minimum of essential tools, could rebuild our industrial complex in a very short time. Even if our industrial plant were totally destroyed in an all-out nuclear attack, properly fed and equipped survivors, living in austerity and working with complete dedication, could rebuild our industrial plant to its pre-attack capacity within five years."

Dr. Herman Kahn is a little less sanguine than Teller but accepts about the same time scale. He estimated in testimony before a Congressional committee that the nation could recover in five years if it suffered a light attack which killed only ten million; with 20 million dead, the recovery time would be ten years; and from a heavy attack (1,000 to 5,000 megatons) which killed 80 million Americans, it would take half a century to recover.

One can only admire the elegant simplicity of the gentlemen's arithmetic. On Dr. Teller's reasoning, with just the know-how and a few essential tools ancient Greece might have leaped into the twentieth century in five years—or China or darkest Africa might today. His glib analysis disregards what it would take to rebuild the complex fabric of an industrial society—an economy in which an electronic gadget produced in a Hoboken plant is made up of a steel chassis fabricated in Chicago, plastic parts from California, gears from New Hampshire, relays from North Carolina, and special transistors from Texas. It has taken a series of five-year plans for the Soviet Union, with its wealth of manpower and raw materials, to build an industrial capacity which does not begin to approach that of the United States. It took Europe a decade, with considerable help from the United States, to get rolling again after the comparatively minor damage of World War II. A nuclear war would not only tear to pieces the organization of our economy but also destroy much of its foundation—including the means of harnessing sources of energy, without which the most sophisticated technology is powerless to rebuild.

Except for Teller-followers and wishful thinkers in the Pentagon, most analysts agree with the view expressed by Walter Lippmann. Speaking of a possible nuclear conflict with the Soviet Union, Mr. Lippmann said that such a war

> "would reduce Soviet society to a smouldering ruin, leaving the wretched survivors shocked and starving and diseased. . . . A nuclear war would be followed by a savage struggle for existence as survivors crawled out of their shelters. . . . A war of that kind would not be followed by reconstruction; it would not be followed by a Marshall plan and by all the constructive things that were done after World War II."

One cannot assume that the survivors would somehow find a way to feed themselves (which Dr. Teller takes for granted). The well-known biologist H. Bentley Glass, a member of the AEC's advisory committee on biology and medicine, believes that even if the entire human population escaped from the attack in shelters, it would emerge afterward into a world barren of practically all life except insects and bacteria. At a "Congress of Scientists on Survival" held in New York, Dr. Glass said:

> "In the absence of fallout shelters for animals, all wild and domestic animals in the combatant countries would be exposed

to lethal doses of radiation. Not only would the meat and milk supply go with the cattle, but an even greater disaster would be the destruction of birds. Without birds to feed on them, the insects would multiply catastrophically. The insects—not man or other proud species—are really the only ones fitted for survival in the nuclear age. They—and bacteria—are enormously radiation-resistant. Let a man absorb 600 roentgens and he perishes soon and miserably, but 100,000 roentgens may not discomfort an insect in the least. The cockroach, a venerable and hardy species, will take over the habitations of the foolish humans, and compete only with other insects or bacteria."

The questions and riddles we have considered are only a sample of the many incalculable factors that bedevil the efforts of the gamesmen and their computers to play a realistic game of nuclear war. We come finally to the most fateful and perplexing question of all: Can a player wait for his opponent to strike first?

Let us start by looking at the proposition from the standpoint of a player who decides he will strike only in retaliation. To deter his opponent, he announces that if the opponent strikes first, he will respond instantly with a massive attack to destroy the opponent's military power. This strategy at once raises a crucial question: How will he seek out that power?

Former Secretary of the Air Force Thomas K. Finletter neatly summarized the dilemma. The attacked nation's retaliatory force (that is, the second-strike force) is pre-aimed at the enemy's military bases. But when it fires the retaliatory strike, many or most of the enemy's missiles have already taken off from those bases for his first strike. The retaliatory mission will hit them too late. In other words, an empty missile shaft is a poor target. And the pre-aimed counter-missile cannot look around for another target. True, the counter-strike presumably is designed to hit all of the enemy's known bases. The enemy's reserve force, however, is likely to be well shielded and difficult to locate. Mr. Finletter's conclusion was: "The job of knocking out the enemy's striking force in our strike-second attack seems, as one thinks of the difficulties, unlikely to succeed."

The only solution, it would appear, is to prepare a force so massive, and so invulnerable to knockout by the enemy, that it threatens a crippling blow to his people and his entire society. "When you strike at a king, you must strike to kill." That means we must outbid the enemy; we must build a force greater than his.

The game now calls for our putting ourselves in his place. What is his reaction to our preparations? Taking everything into account, is he not likely to conclude that we are getting prepared to make the first strike, in case our interests should demand it? Our U-2 reconnaissance and our compilation of a list of targets in the Soviet Union may well have given the Soviet leaders such an impression. The Soviet strategists, like ours, must be prepared for the worst, and the worst is to assume that we will strike first.

Thus, even if neither player starts with the intention of striking first, each may ultimately reach the conclusion that he must do so for self-preservation.

To most Americans it seems inconceivable that our country would start a nuclear war. Our responsible leaders have repeatedly assured the world to the contrary. President Eisenhower declared to the United Nations in 1960: "United States forces exist only for deterrence and defense—not for surprise attack." President Kennedy reaffirmed this position in his first message on national security to Congress: "Our arms will never be used to strike the first blow in any attack."

In an article in the *Saturday Evening Post* of March 27,

1962, titled "Kennedy's Grand Strategy," the writer Stewart Alsop quoted the President as saying in an interview that "in some circumstances we might have to take the initiative." The White House promptly denied, however, that there had been any change in Kennedy's position.

Unfortunately no assurances, however often repeated, will convince the enemy that we will never strike the first blow. As long as we are armed with a killing force which stands poised to strike, he must feel in great danger of being attacked. Our attack might be launched by inadvertence, in response to false information that he is launching a strike against us. It might be set off in a spasm of mass hysteria such as has so often in the past driven nations to rash, impulsive acts because its people were, to quote Walter Lippmann, "frightened, impatient, frustrated, and in search of quick and easy solutions."

This spirit is not absent in our country. We have our "cold warriors" who are impatient for a hotter war—our retired military officers, civilian militarists, columnists, and superpatriots of every description who see no out but a "preventive" attack upon the Soviet Union. While this lunatic fringe need not, perhaps, be taken seriously, there have been many statements by Americans in authority which the Soviet Union may well interpret as advocating a first strike.

In 1959 Defense Secretary Neil McElroy declared that, while the United States' "present policy" was not to strike the first blow, "whether that will always be true is another matter." M. A. MacIntyre, then Undersecretary of the Air Force, said in a speech that "it would be wrong to assume . . . we must accept the first blow on the continental United States." Robert Sprague, a member of the board that drafted the influential Gaither Report prescribing a strategy for the United States, said on a television program: "If war appears to be imminent . . . it is absolutely essential we strike first if we possibly can." And among many similar expressions in Congress is this statement in a House of Representatives report on the Defense Appropriations Bill for 1961:

> "In the final analysis, to effectively deter a would-be aggressor we should maintain our armed forces in such a way and with such understanding that, should it ever become obvious that an attack upon us or our allies is imminent, we can launch an attack before the aggressor has hit us or our allies."

Spokesmen for the Soviet Union, for their part, have talked in similar vein. The Russian threat to defend Fidel Castro's regime in Cuba with "rockets" struck a chill throughout the world, even though it was an obvious bluff. In the opinion of George F. Kennan, former United States Ambassador to Moscow, who is one of the best-informed Americans on Soviet thinking, the possibility of a first strike by the U.S.S.R. is by no means excluded. Mr. Kennan discussed this subject in executive-session hearings of a Senate committee on "organizing for national security" in 1960; the record of the hearings was not published until 1962.

Speaking of the building of a powerful striking force by the United States, Mr. Kennan said: "If the Soviet leaders are ever put into a position by us, knowingly or deliberately or otherwise, where they believe war to be both inevitable and imminent, then I think we can expect them to try to choose the time of its beginning rather than to let that flow from the course of events. . . . This is where we must watch the shaping of our own defense preparations extremely carefully, because if these preparations are of such a nature as to give the Russians this impression, we may produce consequences we didn't want to produce."

The suggestion, inherent in our preparations, that we might hit first is, to be sure, a part of the posture of deterrence. The point I am making is that, because the advantage of the first strike is so great, the policy of deterrence through superior power is essentially self-defeating. The policy works to prevent war only when both sides are convinced that the other will never strike first. They cannot acquire that confidence; on the contrary, as the race to outbid each other in deterrent power goes on, and as tension builds up, the temptation to try to avoid doom by striking the opponent first with a knockout blow becomes more and more compelling. In other words, the deterrence "race" pushes both the United States and the U.S.S.R. closer and closer to the verge of contemplating a first strike.

Certainly this is the way the nuclear game of the two giant powers looks to the rest of the world. It explains the efforts of Britain and France to develop their own nuclear force. In part their motive is to regain their position as major powers in the world and—particularly in Charles de Gaulle's case—to assert their independence in international politics. But quite plainly their purpose also is to have a stronger say about the starting of a nuclear war. To put it bluntly, they seek to deter the United States from taking precipitate action on its own. De Gaulle, it appears, also wishes to possess an independent nuclear force so that France may have the power of initiative in deciding when and where nuclear weapons are to be used.

Defense Secretary McNamara, in his 1962 commencement speech at Michigan, took pains to present a detailed argument against independent nuclear action by our fellow members in NATO. A weak nuclear force, he affirmed, would not be a deterrent against the Soviet Union, and it might invite "a pre-emptive first strike" against a nation (*i.e.*,

France) that proposed to use it independently. The Secretary in this speech made a fervent appeal to the United States' allies to adhere to a common strategy and rely on American nuclear power to protect them from attack.

The speech again emphasized the peril of what has come to be known in nuclear-game parlance as the "nth-country problem." Each new country joining the nuclear club multiplies the chances of an outbreak of nuclear war. When China enters the club on the Communist side (probably creating a conflict of strategies in that camp), and when non-allied countries begin to make their own nuclear weapons, nuclear gamesmanship will fall into chaos. Not even the computer, in its most advanced form, can handle so complex a problem. Strategies collapse; populations vanish; psychologists retire in bafflement; and voodooism takes over. Confusion, to borrow a term from the experts, is maximized.

Perhaps the wisest comment on nuclear gamesmanship was made by Richard B. Russell, the chivalrous Senator from Georgia.

"The day of the tournament," he wryly told the Senate, "has long since passed into history."

# 9

## *Is Defense Possible?*

There are two possible ways of coping with a nuclear weapon winging its way toward you: one is to try to destroy it before it arrives ("active" defense), the other to get behind something very solid ("passive" defense). Specifically these two methods spell (1) anti-missile missiles and (2) shelters. What are the prospects of developing defenses capable of blunting a nuclear attack?

Opinion seems to be sharply divided. Military men such as Lieutenant General Arthur G. Trudeau, chief of Army Research and Development, and Lieutenant General Stanley R. Mickelsen, head of the Army Air Defense Command, are confident that, to quote Mickelsen: "We can establish a defensive system that will nullify the best efforts of the most powerful aggressor."

On the other hand, most scientists think otherwise.

Dr. Hans Bethe believes that the AICBM (anti-ICBM) is "virtually hopeless." The late John von Neumann held that offensive weapons have become so effective that defense can never catch up. He said: "Today there is every reason to fear that even minor inventions and feints in the field of nuclear weapons can be decisive in less time than would be required to devise specific countermeasures."

Let us see where countermeasures stand.

The first link in our defensive system is BMEWS (Ballistic Missile Early Warning System). Consisting of three huge radar installations ringing the Arctic on the Western Hemisphere side—at Clear in Alaska, Thule in Greenland, and Flyingdales Moor in Yorkshire, England—this is designed to give us 15 to 20 minutes' warning of a missile attack launched from the Soviet Union. It would not detect missiles fired at the United States from another direction—for example, from submarines in the Pacific. And it would spot ICBMs only at the height of their arc in space, halfway to their targets. Research is being done on a system of space satellites, called Midas, which might pick up Soviet ICBMs at take-off, by means of infrared sensors detecting the heat of the rocket exhausts. But this project presents serious technological difficulties and in any case would extend the warning time only to half an hour.

The BMEWS stations are elaborate affairs; the Thule installation alone cost $500 million. Their radar antennas are 165 feet high and longer than a football field. They lack fine discrimination, therefore cannot immediately distinguish between an ICBM and, say, a meteor or a sputnik. Their function is simply to detect suspicious objects in the sky and pass them on to "acquisition" radars in the United States which track them further. These radars, sending out an enormously powerful beam from a 50-million-watt transmitter, can track ICBMs up to 1,000 miles away. But at that distance the ICBM, traveling at 15,000 miles per hour, is already less than four minutes from its target!

The time for interception is very short. At the anti-missile base, where a Nike-Zeus will be shot to intercept, target-tracking radars (TTR) lock onto the missile's course and feed the information to high-speed computers, which plot its trajectory. The Nike-Zeus is then launched to meet the ICBM at a certain point in space well short of the target. Guided by a computer, the Nike missile is kept on the track of the ICBM by means of a radar which follows the Nike and feeds instructions to its computer.

How good are the chances for interception? In tests in the Pacific, the Nike-Zeus has scored hits on Atlas missiles. General Trudeau spoke of the game as catching missiles with "our Zeus fielder's glove." But in an actual case of ICBM attack, as opposed to this experimental exercise, the situation would be much less simple. The fielder then would be hard put even to find his way to the right ballpark! Or, to change the analogy, it would be like the difference between shooting at a target in a brightly-lit shooting gallery and trying to hit a swift hawk in a dark marsh on a cloudy night.

Consider the radars, the "eyes" of the defense. Their screens will show objects moving across the sky, but they cannot tell exactly what the objects are. As Dr. Bethe has pointed out:

"The offense can fire a salvo of many missiles simultaneously, and this will saturate the radars so that they can no longer find the right target. And most important, the offense can send, together with the actual missiles, a lot of decoys—gadgets which look to the radars, and maybe also the eye, just the same as a missile, and I can assure you, because I have worked on this problem, that it is extremely difficult to find any way to tell them apart. For these reasons, I believe there is no effective AICBM system."

There are many confusion tactics open to the offense. It may set off nuclear explosives in the sky ahead of the attacking missiles to create a cloud of debris that blurs the vision of the radars. It may arrange to break up the warhead casing and release a flock of smaller warheads—the buckshot approach. The possibilities for "spoofing" or circumventing the radars are almost unlimited.

Let us assume that the problem of identifying and tracking the true warhead is solved somehow, and the Zeus is sent on its mission of interception. A direct hit of the ICBM is extremely improbable; it is like trying to shoot down a bullet with a bullet. The best the defense can hope to do is come within a reasonable "kill" distance of the 16,000-miles-per-hour ICBM.

The Nike-Zeus is a solid-fuel, three-stage missile with a total of 450,000 pounds of thrust. Its closing speed is believed to be sufficient to intercept an ICBM well above the earth's surface.

How would a Zeus kill a nuclear warhead? This problem has not yet been put to a test; the Atlas missiles shot down in the Pacific carried no warheads and were simply blasted apart in the atmosphere. An attacking warhead would have to be intercepted in space, in order to be stopped short of doing damage. In the vacuum of space there is no blast effect, for the airless medium cannot transmit pressure. Two general approaches to killing an ICBM in space might be tried. One is to throw a destructive obstacle in its path. This need not be anything more than a cloud of fine pellets

—a kind of sandstorm. A missile hitting these pellets at 16,000 miles per hour would be riddled and broken up. However, the Zeus shot would have to be very accurate to lay the sandstorm in the ICBM's path.

The other weapon that might stop an ICBM is nuclear radiation, which would have a considerably greater range. The Zeus carries a nuclear warhead. Its explosion in space would release a flood of X-rays, gamma rays, and neutrons. In the absence of air, the effects of a nuclear explosion are different from those in the atmosphere: instead of being absorbed by atoms and producing heat, the nuclear radiations fly unimpeded through space. Now soft X-rays from the Zeus explosion might heat up the ICBM's heat shield and burn off enough of it so that the warhead would burn up when it entered the atmosphere. Assuming that the ICBM nose had a standard heat shield, I would calculate that a Zeus might score an X-ray kill of this kind at a distance of somewhat more than one mile.

The gamma rays from the Zeus explosion offer another possible means of intercepting an ICBM, but probably less effective. These rays might trigger the warhead's firing system so that it destroyed itself in space. The mechanism in the bomb we used at Nagasaki would have been vulnerable to gamma rays. But the enemy could easily devise an electronics system which would counter this defense; he might even let the gamma rays trigger the warhead, merely making the weapon so powerful that it would spread wide damage over the area above which it exploded.

Finally, there is the "neutron kill." The burst of fast neutrons from the Zeus explosion could penetrate an ICBM warhead and fission many of its uranium atoms. This would heat up the bomb material, and the "cooking" might distort it sufficiently to make the bomb a dud. From a Zeus armed with a one-megaton warhead, the flux of neutrons might kill an ICBM at a distance of about a mile.

Even this brief listing of some of the difficulties suggests how problematical the whole theory of anti-missile defense is. To be sure, it may be possible to solve some elements of the problem. The development of more sensitive detection devices might succeed in distinguishing missile warheads from spurious objects; methods of killing the warheads undoubtedly can be devised. But the offense can counter each answer with a trick of its own, and, as Dr. Bethe remarks, "the offense always has many more possibilities than the defense." Moreover, one successful gadget does not make an invulnerable system; a defense system must depend on many links, and one weak link will make it ineffectual.

So far the Nike-Zeus is the United States Army's only anti-missile weapon, and admittedly no better one is in sight. To prepare a gadget of its complexity for operational use takes years of design, engineering, manufacture, and testing. By the time it is ready, the technology of attack may have pulled far ahead, making the defense instrument obsolete.

There is also the bewitching question of how the anti-missile defenses shall be deployed. To build a ring of AICBM bases entirely around the United States would be of questionable value, even if the nation could afford it. Each Nike-Zeus installation may run to $100 million. Where, then, should we place them? Should we defend our ICBM silos and leave our cities unprotected? And if we decide to defend the cities, too, what is the cut-off point: what cities will be left beyond the pale, and how will their inhabitants (and their Congressmen) take this outrage?

Estimates of the cost of a system of Nike-Zeus bases to defend all the major targets in the United States run as high as $60 billion. This would be a rather expensive gamble for a system whose effectiveness is questionable, and by the time it was completed, late in the 1960's, it might be hopelessly outmoded by advances in the offense. Nevertheless, the Zeus system has great popular appeal. Anything that promises a defense against nuclear attack seems worth pursuing, even if it is an illusion. The project also has a powerful, immediate appeal to industry. The initial work on the Zeus has meant contracts for some 80 companies in 17 states. The billions of dollars that would be spread around for an all-out AICBM program offer a lure that is bound to win strong support, in Congress as well as in industry.

There is little doubt that the defense effort would impel a step-up of the offense, for a nation with a shield against retaliation would be in a better position to attack. An accelerated program in each country to increase the strength of its striking force to counter the shield would certainly follow. And military strategists would be inspired to dream up new and more imaginative methods of attack.

To take a concept which is only moderately fanciful, imagine an advance upon our West Coast by six large enemy submarines, each armed with a G-bomb (i.e., a bomb of 1,000 megatons). Patrolling off our shores in the Pacific, the submarines could actually announce their presence, pointing out that any attempt to attack them with depth charges would automatically detonate their bombs. What effects would the explosion of the six giant bombs produce?

As a starter, such a bomb could generate a tidal wave

which would inundate Los Angeles and other coastal cities. But the main power of the weapons would go into a great, lethal cloud of radioactivity which the prevailing westerly winds would spread over most of the United States west of the Mississippi. Although much of the radioactivity would have decayed by the time the fission debris fell to the ground, it would still be deadly enough to wipe out life over vast areas. Even two weeks after the explosion many of the western states would be uninhabitable above ground, and some areas would be dangerous for months.

We need not suppose that the eastern part of the country would escape; presumably the G-submarines would be only a part of the striking force and the enemy would have made provision for threatening the rest of the country as well.

The soaring imagination of our Air Force (and of military airmen in the Soviet Union) has conceived of more interesting methods of attack. Orbiting space stations, manned or unmanned, might circle the earth literally holding swords of Damocles over the enemy's head. Our Defense Department, indeed, is exploring a Buck Rogers-type scheme known as Project Bambi (Ballistic Missile Booster Interceptor). This concept proposes to watch the enemy from space and shoot at his ICBMs as soon as they leave their launch pads. The space stations would dispatch missiles to intercept the ICBMs while they were still in the atmosphere, so that the interceptors' blast could either destroy them or knock them off course during their two minutes of booster flight. It has not yet been explained how the authors of the idea propose to saturate the sky with enough space stations to cope with swarms of ICBMs and leave no loopholes for the enemy to shoot through.

Some airmen foresee a war for space supremacy, with orbital fortresses from which space knights will sally forth to do battle in dogfights in the wild black yonder. The one comfort that earthmen may find in this fantasy is that the battles would cause no scars on the earth below—unless the spacemen violated the rules and unloaded their weapons on the non-combatant planet.

For both offense and defense there remains the ultimate comic-strip weapon—"death rays." General Curtis E. LeMay, the Air Force Chief of Staff, has made known that the Air Force is not overlooking the possibility of "beam-directed energy weapons" which would "strike with the speed of light" and neutralize any missile.

"Suppose the Soviets," General LeMay asked, "were the first to develop advanced weapons of this sort and to employ them aboard maneuvering spacecraft. I don't think it is an exaggeration to say that with such a capability an enemy would have the potential to dominate the world."

Let us pass on from "active" (one might say "over-active") defense to the problems of "passive" defense— that is, hiding the population in underground shelters. We have learned over the years that this is as much a political and social problem as a technical one. It raises questions of many kinds. How effective would shelters be? How many lives could they save? Who should build them? Should we have only fallout shelters, or shelters strong enough to protect against blast and heat as well? Could shelters save city populations?

Would a shelter program look like preparation for war and thus create an atmosphere of tension in which war might become more likely?

The issue of shelters has been discussed spasmodically

in the United States ever since we ceased to be the world's only nuclear power. From time to time the Government has made gestures toward civil defense. But the fading and silly "EVACUATION ROUTE" signs on highways leading out of our cities, the pointless wailing of sirens in periodic "alert" tests, the dormant grass-roots CD organization nominally enlisting everyone from mayors to volunteer firemen—all this only emphasizes the play-acting aspects of our approach to civil defense.

The first serious effort to launch a shelter program was initiated by President Kennedy in 1961. He took this step after returning from his conversations with Nikita Khrushchev in Vienna on the Berlin crisis. The President took pains to explain in his address to Congress that he proposed shelters only as "insurance" against the possibility of "an irrational attack" or accidental nuclear war. He assigned responsibility for civil defense to the Defense Department and instructed it to work out a program, for which he requested an appropriation of $207 million.

Ardent civil defenders took the cue to come forth with optimistic announcements of what shelters could accomplish. *Life* Magazine had claimed that shelters would save 97 per cent of the population in a nuclear attack. Dr. Teller asserted, somewhat more conservatively: "I firmly believe that 90 per cent of our population could be saved." Dr. Willard F. Libby, a nuclear scientist and former member of the AEC, estimated that 90 to 95 per cent could survive with "proper protection." In newspaper articles he prescribed "proper protections" that every householder could build himself, and in the back yard of his own home in the Bel-Air section of Los Angeles he constructed a $30 shelter of railroad ties and bags of soil. Unfortunately, a brush fire which swept through this area of Los Angeles not long afterward left his shelter a charred ruin.

In December 1961 the Department of Defense issued a much-delayed, much-rewritten publication titled "FALLOUT PROTECTION—What to Know and Do About Nuclear Attack." This cheery document turned out to be far from the "clear look at nuclear war" it purported to be.

By the spring of 1962 the Defense Department had begun to spell out a program, estimated to cost some $6 billion. The program was restricted to providing shelter against fallout. The Department located "shelter spaces" for some 60 million people in buildings in metropolitan areas, and it proposed to stock them with a two-weeks supply of food and other necessities. For this, and for community shelters to be built in schools and other public buildings, President Kennedy asked $700 million from Congress.

Deputy Secretary of Defense Roswell L. Gilpatric said that six months of studies, "some of which cannot be fully discussed in public for security reasons," had established that fallout shelters would be of great value. He explained:

> "In general, under a wide variety of attacks which might be possible over the next several years, it appears from present conservative estimates that 40 to 55 million persons who would otherwise be killed could be expected to survive as a result of a system of fallout shelters sufficient to meet the national requirements and backed up by widespread local organization and knowledge of how to use the shelters."

Mr. Gilpatric gave no information that might enable the public to judge the validity of the studies he mentioned. What weight of attack did the estimators have in mind? Did they assume that the attacks would be on cities or on military bases? How many people did they estimate would be killed? What assumptions did they make about warning time, the ability of people to reach shelters, the kinds of shelters available, and so forth? In short, what data did they feed into the computers that gave them their answer?

During Congressional hearings on civil defense in 1961, experts testified that a 3,000-megaton attack on the United States might cause 70 million deaths if 90 per cent of the weight of the attack was aimed at *military* targets. This suggests that 40 to 55 million might be saved by fallout shelters only if cities were spared the main weight of the attack. In the event of a massive attack upon our cities, fallout shelters could not possibly accomplish any such saving of life.

Our military leaders do not assume that cities will not be attacked. Indeed, the whole rationale and the nature of nuclear war make it inevitable that cities *will* be attacked —if not by the first strike, then certainly by those that follow. For that reason, a "fallout only" shelter program makes little sense. If we are to build shelters, the only program that has any logic is to make shelters which might protect our people against the various hazards of nuclear attack. Fallout shelters certainly would save many lives in outlying areas. But a shelter program which leaves our great centers of population really defenseless is hardly more than a gesture.

Something can be said for the protection that might be offered by truly strong shelters. At Hiroshima 43 per cent of the occupants of the sturdy Nippon Bank Building, less than a fifth of a mile from ground zero, survived the bomb. In the Central Telephone Office, a quarter of a mile from ground zero, 87 per cent of the occupants survived. Scaling everything upward to what would be necessary to give blast protection against megaton bombs, it is possible to calculate the requirements of a shelter program which would substantially reduce the impact of a nuclear attack. A shelter that could withstand an overpressure of more than 25 pounds per square inch would protect against the blast from a 20-megaton bomb if it were beyond 3.3 miles from ground zero. On that basis, I believe it would be feasible, and not fantastically expensive, to build a system of blast shelters for our metropolitan areas and fallout shelters for the rest of the country.

But this technical question, as I have mentioned, is only one aspect of a vastly complex problem. Among many other aspects, one must consider the strategic effects. General Lyman L. Lemnitzer, chairman of the Joint Chiefs of Staff, welcomed the fallout-shelter program as "an essential element" of our "deterrent"—that is, our military power. There can be no doubt that a large-scale shelter program would intensify the arms race, leading to Russian shelter-building and the pyramiding of more and bigger weapons by both sides. Shelters would then become part of a vicious circle in strategic thinking.

From the birth of the atomic bomb, I have been an advocate of civil defense. My feeling is simply that history does not encourage us to believe that war will never come again, and if it should come, by accident or intention, we would be better off inside a shelter than outside. But I also have an equally strong feeling that a national program of shelters might inspire a false sense of security. Worse than that, shelters might indeed become a strategic weapon. In the last analysis, the only shelter, the only defense, in which mankind can find any real, enduring hope is disarmament.

# 10

## *Accident, Miscalculation, or Madness*

When President Kennedy advised the United Nations in 1961 that nuclear war might be precipitated "at any moment by accident, miscalculation, or madness," he was speaking feelingly about certain new realities the world had never met before. These were not idle or hysterical words. As President he had been initiated into a chamber of horrors. The possibilities of annihilation by accident, miscalculation, or madness were spelled out to him in vivid detail.

He was the first President to be confronted with this nightmare. President Eisenhower had not had to face the actual possibility that doomsday might come with the suddenness of a thunderclap. In the pre-ICBM era there was at least a little time for considered decision—for investigation, identification of the aggressor, warning, and the launching of defensive measures appropriate to the aggression.

Even the SAC bombers patrolling the skies with nuclear warheads in their bays had a "fail-safe" system. In an emergency (that is, an apparent attack by the Soviet Union) they might be sent toward enemy targets, but they were not to complete their mission unless they received positive orders to do so. As explained by General Thomas S. Power, the commander of SAC, this system gave "the civilian decision-making machinery" (the President and his advisers) at least an hour and a half to investigate whether the United States was actually being attacked. If it was, the bomber crews would receive an order from the President, transmitted in a "fool-proof and safe way," to proceed to the targets and drop their nuclear bombs. If the alarm proved to be spurious, the order would be withheld. In the absence of the order, the bombers had to turn back, whether or not they heard from the commander.

The ICBM has reduced the time for decision to a quarter of an hour. What is more, it has made it extremely difficult, as we shall see, to decide what sort of attack is underway, who the attacker is, and whether the attack is intentional or an accident.

In 1946 the late Louis Ridenour, an able and imaginative physicist, wrote a remarkably prophetic little play called "The Pilot Lights of the Apocalypse." Its setting is a missile command post deep underground. The President of the United States visits the post and has the following colloquy with the Brigadier General in command:

> THE PRESIDENT: . . . General, have you had any exciting times here you can tell me about?
> BRIGADIER: Yes, sir. Every time a meteorite comes

down—a shooting star, you know—our radar boys track it, shoot it down, and send us in an alert. We have a few bad moments until we get a spectrographic report. If it's iron and nickel—as it always has been so far—we know God sent it, and relax. Some day it'll be uranium, and then we'll have to push a button.

In the play the world's major cities are identified by lights on a board, and a red light flashes when a city is destroyed. San Francisco suddenly goes red, attacker unknown. The General excitedly turns to his aides.

BRIGADIER: First we need an enemy. Who's got the highest negative rating in the latest State Department digest?

The world has not yet arrived at this hair-trigger set-up, but we are uncomfortably close to it. Moreover, the button-pushing decision is not as neat as it was in the play, where the defenders killed one city of the enemy in retaliation and waited to see what he would do next. In the actual circumstances now facing the nuclear powers—the existence of overwhelming strike forces, the strategy of massive deterrence and massive retaliation—pressing the button is an act of total war. The President would have to take his decision with the paralyzing knowledge that, by pressing it, he would not only destroy the enemy nation but also condemn tens of millions of his own countrymen to retaliatory death.

Under the Atomic Energy Act, only the President can order a nuclear attack. President Kennedy has set up elaborate safeguards to prevent accidental or unauthorized firing of nuclear weapons. But no system can be made 100 per cent foolproof. Near-disastrous accidents involving nuclear bombs have occurred within the United States and overseas.

And there is an ever-present hazard that somewhere in a critical spot nuclear weapons may go off in defiance of all precautions.

The White House, the State Department, the Pentagon, and the Congress have grown more and more apprehensive about this possibility. In the fall of 1961 Senator Hubert Humphrey introduced in the United States Senate a resolution urging the nations possessing nuclear weapons to tell what precautions they were taking "to prevent accidental nuclear conflict." His resolution noted that nuclear weapons might be fired "through mechanical error, faulty human interpretation of warning signals, issuance of irreversible commands by an undesignated individual," etc. It also noted that a small war with conventional weapons "might, without the decision of supreme authority, start a chain reaction leading unintentionally to a combatant's use of nuclear and thermonuclear weapons."

Secretary of State Dean Rusk, in a speech on June 16, 1962, urging serious disarmament negotiations, said: "The danger of outbreak of war by accident . . . grows as modern weapons become more complex, command and control difficulties increase, and the premium is on ever-faster reaction."

Premier Khrushchev spoke in the same vein at a Soviet-sponsored World Conference on General Disarmament and Peace on July 11, 1962: ". . . [the accumulation of weapons] is reaching the critical point where, as we used to say, the guns start speaking of their own volition, and, as we can now say, where rockets with thermonuclear warheads will start flying."

The possibility of nuclear war "by accident, miscalculation, or madness" has many facets. It is worth while to look at each of them in turn.

According to a study of the accident problem made by an independent, non-military group, nuclear weapons have been involved in about a dozen major incidents or accidents, mostly plane crashes, both in the United States and overseas. In one of these incidents, a B-52 bomber had to jettison a 24-megaton bomb over North Carolina. The bomb fell in a field without exploding. The Defense Department has adopted complex devices and strict rules to prevent the accidental arming or firing of nuclear weapons. In this case the 24-megaton warhead was equipped with six interlocking safety mechanisms, all of which had to be triggered in sequence to explode the bomb. When Air Force experts rushed to the North Carolina farm to examine the weapon after the accident, they found that five of the six interlocks had been set off by the fall! Only a single switch prevented the 24-megaton bomb from detonating and spreading fire and destruction over a wide area.

One wonders what sort of alarm would have been sounded if it had exploded, or if such a bomb had fallen on a city. In the instant of the explosion, it might well have been mistaken by nearly everyone as signalling a surprise attack by the Soviet Union.

Intercontinental missiles present a much more critical problem. The accidental firing of a United States ICBM would send it irrevocably on its way to a Soviet target. Accordingly, the ICBMs are surrounded with many safeguards.

The Minuteman, housed in an unattended silo and always ready for instant launching, is an especially hazardous problem, on two counts: it might go off by accident, or it might be tampered with by saboteurs or fired by fanatics stealing into the site. A number of special safety measures have been devised for it. The missile has a series of arming switches. It cannot be fully armed for detonation until after it leaves its silo, for the final switch is closed only by the strong force of acceleration that speeds it away from the earth. The site is constantly under electronic surveillance, so that an intruder would set off an alarm. There are precautions against many other contingencies, including the possibility that the two officers manning the control room might go berserk and try to launch the missile against orders.

The safety system is in considerable part the result of a special study ordered by President Kennedy; a committee of experts examined the Minuteman set-up and recommended safety improvements to cover every conceivable accident, error, or malfunction. Yet all the safety factors, the President later concluded, still left a serious loophole in the control of ICBMs. It is summed up in the military term "command and control."

The problem has been stated most succinctly by Lloyd V. Berkner, organizer of the International Geophysical Year and one of the most humane and respected United States scientists. In an article in *Foreign Affairs* in 1958 he observed:

> "As large numbers of fast-flying missiles come into the possession of both sides, ready for use, critical command will tend to devolve to lower and lower echelons. To some extent this is already occurring. If we are going to be able to retaliate effectively, it will become less and less practicable to assemble the Congress or to call together the Cabinet or even for the President to be consulted when missiles with the ultimate destructive power are seen flying toward us."

In other words, in the era of missile warfare the control of nuclear weapons steadily becomes more diffuse, and the danger of war through accident, miscalculation, or madness must rise correspondingly. As Charles E. Osgood, president of the American Psychological Association, has pointed out, the maintenance of peace depends upon rational behavior by those in control; yet in the present era of great danger we are more than ever at the mercy of "the unpredictability of human behavior under stress." This unpredictability applies equally to chiefs of state and to lower echelons. But with the diffusion of control of nuclear weapons to more and more hands, the chances of someone breaking under the stress are multiplied.

President Kennedy became concerned about the problem of command and control soon after taking office. United States missiles and nuclear weapons are in many different hands and many different places. Furthermore, some are at the potential disposal of military forces of other countries. Stockpiles of nuclear warheads are available, for example, at bases of the West German Air Force. Though in the custody of United States military units, these weapons may be turned over to the Germans in an "emergency."

Alarmed by the grim possibilities, President Kennedy and the Joint Congressional Committee on Atomic Energy set out to establish firmer control of nuclear weapons by the President. One safeguard they recommended was an electronic device. It is a "safety lock" designed to control the arming of United States nuclear warheads everywhere in the world by remote control from command centers. Like a portable channel switcher for a television set, the device uses a coded radio signal to actuate a switch releasing the bomb detonator for firing. Without this signal, authorized by the President, the bomb cannot be fired—in theory, but resourceful electronics experts might find a way. President Kennedy asked the Congress on July 5, 1962, for a supplementary appropriation of $23 million to the Atomic Energy Commission so that the device could be installed on missile warheads.

No matter how secure against accident our bombs may be made, we must still reckon with the possibility of a Soviet accident. We do not know what precautions, if any, the U.S.S.R. high command has taken. If a Soviet ICBM earmarked for an American city were accidentally fired, if a Soviet missile in a testing exercise went astray, the result could be as disastrous as the accidental firing of one of ours.

Nuclear war might be touched off by another kind of spark.

At 10:35 on the morning of February 2, 1947, the people of Novopokrovka, a village in eastern Siberia some hundreds of miles from Vladivostok, were alarmed by a strange visitor from space. A ball of light as bright as the sun passed swiftly across the sky, flew south, and plunged to earth in nearby mountains with a tremendous explosion. The spectacular phenomenon brought scientists from Moscow to investigate. They found a scene of weird devastation: a forest felled, rocks shattered, craters 30 to 40 feet deep, and the ground strewn with huge chunks of iron. Some trees had been thrown miles into the air by the gigantic explosion.

The place had been struck by an asteroid—a small asteroid some 30 feet in diameter and weighing about a thousand tons. Had it fallen on a city, it might have simulated a nuclear attack. San Francisco, or New York, would have flashed the red light on Dr. Ridenour's board.

This incident took place before the ICBM era. It is not restful to think about how such an event might be received today—if, for example, a large meteorite fell on a metropolis or a missile base in either the United States or the Soviet Union. Of course, meteoritic visitors of this size are rare, but the chances are not vanishingly small, as is evidenced by the many large craters on the earth (and on the moon). And smaller meteorites are a common occurrence—common enough to appear with some frequency on the radar scopes of our warning systems. With good reason General Power, the SAC commander, was constrained to say: "I cannot see for the foreseeable future how we can launch [retaliatory missiles] on the basis of radar detection alone."

We may take some comfort from such statements. Indeed, in a time of relatively unexcited international relations all the imagined accidents seem nothing more than morbid speculation. Surely nations would not go to war because of a falling meteorite or a single explosion! Perhaps not, but one does not like to think about the possibilities if such an incident should occur during an acute crisis—say an ultimatum on Berlin or Red Chinese preparations to invade Formosa or the outbreak of a bitter local war. In a situation of high tension every incident, every rumor, would make the world suddenly conscious of the ICBMs waiting to be launched—and the machinery of striking (in retaliation or pre-emptively) would shift into high gear.

It is painful to speculate on how the "decision-making machinery" might respond to a megaton warhead falling on one of our cities. It might be an accidental drop from a United States bomber; it might even conceivably be a deliberate detonation by a group of insane superpatriots seeking to provoke a retaliatory attack upon Communist Russia. Hopefully, the true source of the explosion might quickly be identified. But suppose it were actually a Soviet ICBM. Suppose that a lone, 20-megaton warhead obliterates, say, St. Louis—or an ICBM site—and our tracking radars have shown beyond doubt that it came from a Soviet launching site.

The news is flashed to the President at the beach in Hyannisport by way of the team of Army officers, equipped with walkie-talkies, who never let him out of their sight. The President is dumbfounded. A Soviet strike by a single ICBM? What can it signify? Is it a warning and a token (*a la* Hiroshima)? Is it the prelude to a general attack? Or is it perhaps an accident—the inadvertent release of a missile earmarked for the target it hit?

The President must take some action. What action? The dilemma was posed at a Congressional committee hearing by Admiral Arleigh Burke, former Chief of Naval Operations:

> ADMIRAL BURKE: . . . What does the President do? . . . It is hard to know. . . . He has a choice. He has the choice of calling up Russia and saying, "Did you mean it?" or he has the choice of launching.

It would take a high degree of self-control to "absorb" the demolition of an American city without killing a Soviet city in return. And yet retaliation would certainly escalate into general war.

One can conceive of many enemy moves which would look like preparations for a major nuclear attack upon us. McGeorge Bundy, special assistant to President Kennedy, has remarked that the number of forms the attack might take "is very large." By the same token, so is the number of possibilities for misinterpretation.

Suppose the Soviet Union suddenly orbited a large flock of sputniks which gave every indication of being warhead carriers. Should we try to destroy them? Or let us say that our Samos satellites or space stations sent down photographs of Soviet missile centers which indicated that they were preparing to launch. Or suppose a more definite warning: a report from our intelligence agents that "all Soviet ICBMs have been ordered to be in a condition of full alert within twelve hours!" The Soviet alert might actually be only a practice exercise, but the President could not assume that this was the case. If the alarm came at the height of a crisis, with both sides making moves toward an apparent showdown, he might have to assume the worst. What action should he take? Should he wait until the Soviet missiles were actually on their way, or should he strike their bases first? Wait for a Pearl Harbor, or try to prevent it? Yet how could he press the button and expose his nation to disastrous retaliation while there was still even a remote chance that the enemy did not intend to attack?

To say the President's position would be unenviable is the feeblest of understatements. No man should be asked, or allowed, to play God. If the position of the President of the United States or the Premier of the Soviet Union is agonizing, it is vastly more intolerable that the survival of mankind should depend on the decision of one or two men or a group of men.

Only nuclear disarmament can extricate humanity from this position. In reality, the men in charge of the push-buttons would have no choice in a major war crisis. No one in the councils of strategy, either in Washington or Moscow, doubts that nuclear weapons would be used if the Western and Communist worlds went to war. Threatened with nuclear attack, the defenders of the warring nations would not hesitate to respond in kind. Their replies would be automatic.

It is important to note that the hazard of a nuclear war being touched off by accident depends a great deal on the nature of the weapons and the way they are deployed. Consider, for example, the case of an apparent missile attack upon the United States—either a single missile hitting a city or a radar indication or intelligence warning that a salvo is on its way. If our retaliatory force consists mainly of ICBMs based within the country, it becomes imperative to launch them before they are struck. The situation is very different if our deterrent force takes the form of Polaris submarines deployed at sea. In that case the force is not in immediate danger and remains intact, so that our decision-making machinery has time to ask "Did you mean it?" if a city is hit or to investigate whether the supposed attack is really what it seems.

In short, a massive striking force of land-based ICBMs creates a greater danger of nuclear war by accident than does a Polaris force. Its existence makes both sides uneasy about the possibility of the opponent striking first to kill the "birds" while they are still in their nests; it compresses the time for decision in a crisis; and it virtually rules out any opportunity for mature thought or investigation.

Many military men, as well as civilians, regard "tactical" nuclear weapons as a still more dangerous Pandora's box of accidents and miscalculations. The manufacture of these weapons, and the Pentagon proposals to use them in limited engagements, are the height of irresponsible nuclear gamesmanship. The first firing of a nuclear weapon in anger, no matter how small the weapon or how remote the battlefield, would kindle alarm and panic throughout the world. This would be especially true if the explosion took place at a point where American and Communist forces confront each other (for example, Quemoy). No electronic "lock" or other safety device on a weapon could be made completely tamper-proof. Can we be sure that some mad or drunken officer will never throw one of these tactical weapons at the enemy in a "brushfire" skirmish? Will the enemy fail to throw one back sooner or later? And where will the exchange then stop?

No one can predict how rapidly and widely a "limited" nuclear engagement would spread, even under the strictest command and control. General Lauris Norstad, the commander of NATO, said in 1959:

> "I do not agree with those people who say that you can control the size of this fire . . . neatly, cold-bloodedly . . . once it starts. I think that it is the most dangerous and disastrous thing in the world. I think that you must prevent the thing from starting in the first place, because once it starts in a critical area, such as the NATO area, it is more likely than not, in my opinion, to explode into the whole thing, whether we like it or the Russians like it or anybody likes it."

Finally, we may ponder the paranoia of an unhappy dictator, brooding beside his push-button. The picture of Adolf Hitler in his last days in the Berlin bunker comes to everyone's mind. He was not unique. History is eloquent on the high incidence of erratic, megalomaniac rulers—installed variously by divine right, by military coup, and by election. Passing the Rorschach test is not a requirement for election to high office, and chiefs of state have seldom been put away in a safe place for their peculiarities, however obvious. We need not necessarily presuppose a truly demented man, whose outlandish orders might be ignored. We have more to fear from the aging, quick-tempered dictator who dreams of one final, grandiose show of power, or from the monomaniac, passionately dedicated to a cause, who is incapable of intelligent, objective judgment. Such a man, in control of nuclear weapons, might demonstrate tragically "the unpredictability of human behavior under stress."

The number of nations with nuclear weapons is slowly but steadily growing. Great Britain and France already have their own. No doubt other countries are doing "research." Soon there will be red telephones and push-buttons elsewhere in the world besides the White House and the Kremlin. Indeed, the partners of the United States in NATO are demanding, and receiving, more nuclear weapons from the stockpile and a larger measure of control over their use. We may be approaching a situation in which there will be "15 fingers on the trigger," with increasing uncertainty about who may press it.

On the other side, it is only a matter of time before China joins the Soviet Union as a nuclear power. No one (including the Soviet Union) looks upon this prospect with anything but disquietude. Of all the big nations, China has the least to lose (in industrial wealth) from a nuclear attack; consequently it is the least likely to be restrained by threats of nuclear retaliation.

Surveying the state of affairs at the opening of the 1960s, C. P. Snow was moved to prophesy: "Within, at the most, ten years, some of these bombs are going off." These may, indeed, be the years of maximum peril.

# 11

## "The Hope of Civilization"

Like many scientists, I have lived close to the atom for more than 20 years. My apprenticeship was served at the University of Chicago with the late Professor A. J. Dempster, who, during the 1930s, had discovered the U-235 isotope of uranium. At the time, fission was unknown, and Dr. Dempster had no idea that the new species of atom he detected with his mass spectroscope would mean so much to humanity. But in the early 1940s, there on the Chicago campus, we saw the birth of the nuclear age.

In the professor's laboratory in Eckhart Hall I worked with him running his atom-separating machine, often spending hours in pitch blackness. Directly above, on the next floor, was the meeting room used by the Metallurgical Laboratory, which produced the first fission chain reaction. We were well aware that the success of the experiment in the uranium pile under the stands of the University Stadium would change the world beyond recall. After hours, a few of us often met to talk about the coming A-bomb and its implications. The deeply concerned scientists—Leo Szilard, James Franck, Eugene Rabinowitch, and others—already had a vivid vision of the hazardous future. We were frightened men, and with good reason.

After the war a number of American scientists joined together in an effort to explain the revolutionary character of the new force and bring it under safe control. The *Bulletin of the Atomic Scientists* set out to make clear to the nation how close the hands of the clock were to midnight for the human race. Scientists journeyed to Washington to plead that atomic energy be placed under civilian rather than military control. In the winter of 1945-46 a motley lobby of professors descended upon Capitol Hill to oppose the May-Johnson Bill (military) and argue for the McMahon Atomic Energy Bill (civilian control). The scientists went from office to office button-holing members of the Congress and explaining the mysteries of atomic energy. Without organization, contacts, or money, but with a spontaneous outpouring of popular support, these Paul Reveres won the passage of the McMahon Act creating the civilian Atomic Energy Commission.

Unhappily, the AEC for which we had fought so hard became a mere servant of military strategy—a weapons-maker that dwarfed all previous munitions industries. The nuclear stockpile grew like Topsy. All the horrors we had foreseen came to pass: armadas of bombers, hordes of ICBMs, and a continuously escalating arms race.

In retrospect, we must lay a great deal of the blame on simple ignorance. Military thinking was still chained to the past. It clung to the myopic view that strength lay in numbers: the more weapons a nation had, the more secure it would be. It is now plain that this was a great illusion. Since World War II the United States has spent more than $600 billion in quest of military security, yet it cannot be said that security has come any closer than before. Indeed, as Secretary of State Rusk has said, we are "enjoying less and less security." What was overlooked was that nuclear weapons introduced a new scale of weights and measures which demolished the old doctrines and gave an entirely new aspect to defense. Through lack of appreciation of that fact, the Pentagon apparently made a gross miscalculation of the relative positions of the United States and the Soviet Union.

The British physicist P. M. S. Blackett has attempted to estimate the comparative nuclear strike forces of the two powers. In an article in *Scientific American,* he presented his surprising results. In 1961 the United States had, according to Defense Secretary McNamara, some 1,700 intercontinental bombers (including 630 B-52s and 1,000 B-47s), about 1,300 shorter-range planes carrying nuclear warheads, several dozen operational ICBMs, about 80 intermediate-range missiles, 80 Polaris missiles, and various other vehicles for delivering nuclear bombs. All told, the number of delivery vehicles was "in the tens of thousands." And the United States stockpile of nuclear weapons was estimated at about 30,000 megatons.

Against this, what was the Soviet arsenal? "Semi-official estimates from Washington," said Blackett, "gave the U.S.S.R. about 150 intercontinental bombers, 50 ICBMs, 400 medium-range missiles, plus some possible submarine missiles and its nuclear-armed fighters (which are too short-range to reach the United States)." The size of the Soviet nuclear-weapons stockpile is a deep mystery, but Blackett estimated that 1,000 megatons would be sufficient to carry out the retaliatory blows the Soviet Defense Minister has boasted he is prepared to inflict upon the United States and its allies.

If the "semi-official estimates" are even approximately correct, the Soviet striking force was astonishingly far below that of the United States. Senator Stuart Symington conceded in 1961 that our intelligence agencies had vastly overestimated the Soviet strength. (Among other things there was no "missile gap.") It became obvious that the U.S.S.R. had relied on a "minimum deterrent"—a force not designed to knock out our striking power but only large enough to destroy our cities and industries if it were attacked. In short, a second-strike force.

Such a doctrine, indeed, is a logical system of defense in the nuclear age. A force sufficient to kill the enemy's population and destroy his wealth is an adequate deterrent. It is as strong a deterrent—or should be—as the threat to destroy his military power. Cities and populations will die in any case—in any massive nuclear attack—for this is the nature of the weapon. The first target struck by a nuclear warhead, let it be remembered, was a city, and no doubt a city will also be the last. Such is the ethos of the thermonuclear bomb. There is no merciful way to fight a nuclear war. And if we must deter with a nuclear threat, let it at least be a deterrent calculated to minimize the opponent's fear that we will strike first.

Unfortunately the evaporation of the missile gap did not slow down the arms race. Indeed, in 1961 the United

States Government stepped up the ICBM program and set its sights on building a maximum deterrent—a force strong enough to annihilate "the enemy's military forces."

The year 1961 marks a turning point in the arms competition. The Soviet Union apparently abandoned the doctrine of the minimum deterrent. We do not know what changed Premier Khrushchev's mind, but whatever other motives he may have had, certainly his decision must have been influenced by the acceleration of ICBM production in the United States and the U-2 overflights probing the Soviet Union's vulnerability to attack. Khrushchev responded by increasing the Soviet military budget substantially and by resuming the testing of nuclear weapons.

"We cannot but take note of the fact," declared Mr. Khrushchev, "that the imperialists are stepping up the arms race, preparing their armed forces for war against us and building up huge stocks of weapons, including nuclear weapons. In the interest of the security of our country and the entire socialist camp, we are compelled to strengthen in every way the might of our armed forces. . . . We shall not let anyone catch us unawares."

And so the arms race has ascended to a higher level. How far will it, or can it, go? Lord Bertrand Russell calculates that the chances are no better than six to four that the world will avoid nuclear war. Some think he is over-optimistic. Must we, then, wait for the throw of the dice? *Que sera, sera?*


"The hope of civilization," said President Truman after Hiroshima, "lies in international arrangements looking, if possible, to the renunciation of the use and development of the atomic bomb. . . . The alternative . . . may be a desperate armament race which might well end in disaster."

Twelve years later, prophecy having become fact, President Eisenhower repeated the appeal: "In the last analysis, there is only one solution to the grim problems that lie ahead. The world must stop the present plunge toward more and more destructive weapons of war and turn the corner that will start our steps firmly on the path toward lasting peace. . . . Of all the works of peace, none is more needed than a real first step toward disarmament."

The Soviet Union has made declarations in equally lofty terms, attributing to itself alone a genuine desire for peace. "General and complete disarmament under strict international control," says the syllabus of the Communist Party, "is a radical way of guaranteeing a durable peace."

Yet a decade and a half of so-called disarmament negotiations has produced nothing but words. As Senator John F. Kennedy observed in 1959: "Disarmament remains a pious phrase which both sides invoke—but which they will not invoke together." Neither side has been willing to make any crucial concession toward agreement. Even the effort to agree on an end to testing nuclear weapons has been frustrated by the erection of straw men by both sides: the Russians insisting that the United States wants only to send spies into the Soviet Union in the guise of inspectors, and the United States insisting upon the most rigorous safeguards to prevent the Russians from cheating (although experiments have now shown that a network of seismograph stations could detect any sizable underground nuclear explosion).

It has been said that the Soviet Union wants disarmament without control, and the United States wants control without disarmament. The truth is a great deal simpler. Both contestants are committed to power politics, and neither will yield an iota of its potential threat to the other.

But like the day of the jousting tournament, the day when nations could enforce their will by resort to arms has passed into history. "Why not victory?" is merely a rhetorical phrase without any real meaning. In a war between nuclear powers there can be no victory. The United States cannot stop communism by nuclear arms without destroying itself, nor can the Soviet Union overthrow capitalism by force without suffering the same fate.

It is not my purpose here to examine the political obstacles to world peace. To be sure, the political problems are critical. There can be no real peace until nations have found a way to resolve or accommodate their differences. In the present atmosphere of acute distrust, general and complete disarmament is indeed a hopeless dream. Yet, if we cannot have disarmament and true peace, we may at least hope for the absence of war—until disarmament becomes feasible. To preserve the absence of war, we must somehow halt the nuclear arms race, for it is steadily intensifying the political conflicts and increasing the chances of a showdown. As President Kennedy has said: "No sane society chooses to commit national suicide. Yet that is the fate which the arms race has in store for us—unless we can find a way to stop it."

How to stop it—that is the life-and-death question of the 1960s. No one supposes that there is any easy or magic formula. It is not likely that the United States and the Soviet Union will suddenly "see the light" together and amiably conclude an agreement. Nevertheless, they share one great interest: they have a common interest in staying alive. Furthermore, both nations have a mutual concern about the future rise of other nuclear powers—notably China and Germany. In the long run a nuclear-armed China would be

143

as great a threat to its neighbor, the U.S.S.R., as to the United States. The present nuclear powers therefore have the strongest motives to bring these weapons under control while there is still time. The time is short. The 1970s will be too late.

If the two sides will not act jointly on steps toward arms control, we must consider whether a start could be made independently. Should the United States, then, take the initiative? To many people, especially some in our Congress, "unilateral action" has become synonymous with treason or stupidity when it means moves toward peace. It cannot be denied that there are risks in such action. Machiavelli cynically observed: "There is nothing more difficult to take in hand, more perilous to conduct, or more uncertain in its success, than to take the lead in the introduction of a new order of things." But the risks of a continuation of the arms race are far greater. What is more, there are steps the United States could take which in all likelihood would improve, rather than endanger, our security.

Let me suggest a few which emerge logically from an objective and realistic analysis of our nuclear hazards.

1. *Our missile program* should be revised to make it a truly retaliatory force rather than one which appears to be prepared for a first strike. The most effective way of doing this would be to place our main reliance on a Polaris force. The program for ICBMs based within the country should be cut back sharply and eliminated altogether as the ocean-deployed Polaris force becomes an adequate deterrent.

Several important strategic gains would be achieved by this policy. Our deterrent force would be less vulnerable to knockout by the enemy. It would not be in positions where it might draw attack upon our land. It would allow us more time for investigation of alarms, thus reducing the chances of war by accident. It would provide more unified command and control of our strategic force. It would obviate any need for maintaining United States missile bases on foreign soil. It would be far less costly, and at the same time safer, than the attempt to build a land-based force of missiles hardened against megaton attack. Putting our missiles underwater would lessen the need to put our population underground. And as a force geared to deterrence, not to overkill, the Polaris program would remove much of the steam from the arms race. In short, it would be a stable deterrent, sufficient for its purpose but not calculated to spur both sides to building stronger and stronger forces for a possible pre-emptive strike. A first strike would be futile: it could not possibly save the attacker from heavy retaliation.

A submarine-based deterrent also lends itself more readily to the next essential steps—international arms control and gradual disarmament. A workable system of control would be less difficult to arrange, from the standpoint of both limitation and inspection. It would be easier to establish quotas, and if both sides were restricted to ocean-going forces, the inspection system could be more reliable and a great deal less objectionable to the parties than one which called for internal combing of each country for possible missile sites hidden underground.

I do not mean to suggest that an overall system of arms control could be worked out in any such simple way; I am merely proposing that a stable deterrent such as I have described offers the best opportunity for ending the arms race and taking the first steps toward agreements reducing the danger of a massive surprise attack.

2. *The unending production of bomb material* by the Atomic Energy Commission should be called off, at long last.

145

It has now gone well beyond 30,000 megatons, and Secretary of State Rusk has estimated that by 1966, at the present rate, the stockpile may double that figure. We already have enough nuclear explosives to overkill the Soviet Union at least 25 times. What earthly justification can there be for piling up any such deluge of destruction? The huge production plants (at Oak Ridge, Hanford, and elsewhere) should be "mothballed." The $2 billion per year thereby saved by the AEC, as well as many of its facilities, may then be devoted to a program of "science and atomic energy for peace," which would vastly enhance the stature of the United States in the world.

3. *The realm of space* should be declared out of bounds for military operations. There are good reasons to believe that an early agreement on this with the Soviet Union would be possible. Responsibility for our experiments in space is now divided between the National Aeronautics and Space Administration and the Air Force, with much duplication of effort and waste of funds. NASA should be given undivided authority over the work with big booster rockets, and the missions of our space vehicles should be concentrated on scientific explorations and peaceful applications, so well exemplified by Telstar, the brilliantly successful communications satellite. The research and operations conducted by NASA should be completely in the open, without secrecy restrictions. If orbiting satellites are to be used for reconnaissance, it should be done openly. Such observation, conducted without concealment by both sides, could be reassuring, rather than alarming, to both parties.

4. *An international communications system* should be set up to check on accidents or incidents that might lead to inadvertent war. This system, operated under the sponsorship of the United Nations, could spread immediate word of

an accidental explosion or missile release; it could be consulted for quick checking of a false alarm or any disturbing event. Such a clearinghouse might well serve as a safety valve, affording some insurance against a nuclear war being touched off through misunderstanding.

5. *A thorough study of the effects of nuclear war* should be made under the auspices of the United Nations. The United States might well take the initiative in carrying out the study and present a full report to the UN for distribution to all nations, including non-members. The purpose of the study would be to make clear to all the peoples of the earth precisely what a nuclear war would mean; the study would examine the biological, ecological, economic, cultural, social, and political consequences. The secretiveness of nuclear testing and weapons development by the military establishments has left the whole subject enshrouded in dark and confusing controversy. There is a widespread impression, fed by reckless nuclear strategists, that it is possible to "win" a nuclear war, at a tolerable cost in casualties. Although the responsible leaders of the United States and the Soviet Union have repeatedly assured the world to the contrary, their warnings have been given only in vague terms. It is high time that the facts on this vital matter were fully and frankly aired.

No doubt to many people—those who like to think of themselves as "hard-headed"—these proposals will seem idealistic and impractical. Others perhaps will regard them as too conservative, scarcely touching the heart of the problem. Admittedly, steps such as I have outlined would be only the beginning of a beginning. In the long run the only "hope of civilization" is, indeed, complete renunciation of the overwhelming new weapons. But we must start somewhere. If we really mean what we say about our desire for nuclear arms control and disarmament, we must begin by abating the fears that inspire the arms race. Limiting our counterforce to truly defensive proportions would go a long way toward creating a climate in which the United States and the Soviet Union could begin to negotiate seriously for arms control.

I am not underestimating the immense difficulty of initiating such an approach here at home. It will require a virtual revolution in the thinking of Congress and the military establishment. More fundamentally, it calls for a readjustment by the nation as a whole. For we are trapped, in a sense, in an arms economy and a weapons culture.

We have created a vast arms industry whose economic and political reach extends into every corner of the nation. Our annual military budget of more than $50 billion generates another $50 billion of economic activity, so that armaments actually account for about one-fifth of our total gross national product. The paychecks of many millions of our workers are certified in the Pentagon. In the State of California more than 750,000 workers owe their jobs directly or indirectly to defense contracts; counting their families, this means that two million people in that state are supported by military work. Utah houses military installations which cost more than $1 billion to build, and its people depend upon more than $500 million a year in defense contracts. These are merely samples of the national picture.

Naturally, every arms cutback or contract cancellation begets a public outcry. When the Defense Department considered cutbacks at the Griffiss Air Force Base in upstate New York, Congressman Samuel S. Stratton denounced the proposal as a "fantastic" mistake which would increase unemployment in his district. When, on the other hand, Congressman Byron Johnson of Colorado voted against a defense bill and campaigned for disarmament in 1960, he was defeated for re-election in his state, where the Titan ICBM is manufactured. Of the three lone Congressmen who voted No on the defense bill, none was re-elected.

It is no wonder that the Congress maintains a militaristic posture. Together with the military establishment and the arms industry, it forms a triangle of great power which controls our national life. Industry and the Pentagon are so closely linked that it is difficult to tell where one ends and the other begins. For example, the General Dynamics Corporation, builder of the Atlas and the recipient in 1961 of more than $1 billion in defense contracts, had in its employ 187 retired officers, including 27 generals and admirals.

Even President (former General) Eisenhower found it necessary in his farewell address to utter a warning against military dominance. He said: "This conjunction of an immense military establishment and a large arms industry is new in the American experience. . . . We must guard against the acquisition of unwarranted influence . . . by the military-industrial complex. The potential for the disastrous rise of misplaced power exists and will persist."

Unless there is a drastic change in the public outlook, the triumvirate of Congress, the military, and industry may condemn the United States to a permanent and ever-growing arms economy. Can our democracy disengage itself from its dependence on military paychecks? Can we disarm without wrecking our economy? It will not be easy. But who will maintain that a nation as rich and resourceful as the United States cannot live except by making weapons?

The problem today is different from what we faced in

returning to a civilian economy after World War II. Then the nation had plenty to do in building housing, automobiles, and all the other goods whose production had been suspended during the war. Today we have no such backlog of private wants to absorb the surplus of our productive capacity. But we do have other great and urgent needs. Our postwar explosion of births cries for more schools, now scandalously overcrowded; our choking, shabby cities need rebuilding; our highways are one great traffic jam; our metropolitan areas cry out for modern transportation; our crowded hospitals must turn patients away; our natural resources need works of conservation if they are not to waste away. A study conducted by the Eisenhower Administration but never released for general distribution is said to have listed needs of $7.5 billion for education, $3.7 billion for public health, $3.2 billion for urban renewal, $4 billion for development of natural resources, and $3 billion for space research. There is no necessity for massive infusions of defense funds to nourish our economy; we could keep our industries humming and our people working on the monumental job of improving the well-being of the body politic.

To the list of proposals for ending the arms race, therefore, I would add these:

I. *The problems of arms control and the transition to a civilian economy* should be made major subjects of study by new United States agencies assigned to these tasks. I suggest that these studies might be carried out by: (1) an Office of Industrial Reorientation, under the Arms Control and Disarmament Agency, to work out plans for a smooth transition to other work as defense contracts are cut back; (2) an Office of Arms Control in the Defense Department to study the adaptability of present and future weapons systems to international control; (3) university groups to study problems of disarmament and the effects of the weapons culture on a free society.

In September 1961 President Kennedy persuaded Congress to authorize the establishment of the United States Arms Control and Disarmament Agency, originally proposed by scientist members of the Democratic Advisory Council. Skeptical and grudging in its support, the Congress slashed the agency's funds shortly after creating it. Because of the hostility of many Congressmen, it is essential that the work of this agency be conducted in full public view, so that its objectives and programs can be understood and supported. The newspaper columnist Marquis Childs has reported that a study of the problem of reconverting arms industries to peaceful production, made by the Senate Foreign Relations Committee, was kept locked in the committee's files because "some Senators believed it might give aid and comfort to the Communists." This is indeed an odd theory of democracy: that we cannot frankly face and deal with our problems because attempts to solve them would strengthen the enemy's propaganda case against us!

I believe that the proposed Office of Industrial Reorientation should work closely with the Defense Department, working out remedial measures not only for economic dislocations that might result from arms control but also for those now caused by cancellations of contracts because of shifts in the Department's program. The Defense Department itself already has some officers assigned to studies of arms control; their efforts, however, need to be organized and coordinated with high-level planning and research.

Informal studies of disarmament have been undertaken at a number of colleges and universities. The Government and private foundations should encourage these studies with financial grants and initiate new ones. There is an acute need for inquiries into how the Congress might be brought to play a more constructive role in arms control and disarmament.

II. *Assistance to the Congress* in dealing with the extraordinarily complex problems of the nuclear age is long overdue. It seems to me vital that the Congress should be equipped with permanent, non-partisan machinery to provide the information and expert counsel it so badly needs. It would be greatly helped, I believe, by the appointment of a Science Council to advise it on atomic, space, and defense problems.

When all is said and done, it is Congress that sits in the main seat of power in our democracy. Without its support, no policy involving our vital interests can be established, changed, or carried out. Our international relations, military strategy, economic structure, arms control, disarmament—all these depend, in the last analysis, on what the Congress is willing to approve or determined to reject. Yet of all the agencies of Government, Congress is the least informed—the rankest layman, or, in a happier phrase, the epitome of the common man. It knows a little about everything and not much about anything. It is not much better equipped to handle issues of science or technology than a television addict or a newspaper reporter on the police beat.

To provide the Congress with guidance on scientific matters, I would propose a Council of nine scientists, each serving a two-year term so that the group would rotate yet maintain a continuity through overlapping of terms. They should be appointed, in my opinion, by the President, in order to be free of Congressional pressure or favor. They would sit as non-voting members on House and Senate committees concerned with scientific activities, and they would provide the Congress with annual reports on scientific issues and developments. The scientists would be selected from those actively engaged in creative research, and they should be free from industrial connections. In making his appointments, the President would be strongly disposed, of course, to choose scientists politically and ideologically pleasing to the Congressional leaders. The scientific community, however, would be a deterrent to bad appointments, for it would not hesitate to raise its voice against the selection of an incompetent or sycophantic scientist.

If our Congress is in need of education, what about the rest of us? The most boastful American must concede that he finds himself at a loss in the strange world that has suddenly overtaken us. He wishes that he understood science better. Although our country is the most advanced in the world in scientific research—and the most richly rewarded —we remain a nation of scientific illiterates. Most of us have a great deal of catching up to do. We cannot long remain ignorant of the forces at work in our society and still survive. But survival in this age of awesome weaponry will demand more than an understanding of science. It will demand a more precise sense of time and numbers and the significance of events, of politics and economics, of man's limitations and his strengths. More than anything else, the world needs a restoration of man's faith in himself as an individual—the confidence that he is the master of his destiny.

The writer Walter Millis has remarked: "A policy which can see no further than a missile-megaton arms race amounts . . . to a disregard of [the] fundamental concepts of the inherent value of the individual, of the dignity and fraternity of all men." It is on individual dignity and fraternity that we must depend for liberation from the nuclear sword dangling over our heads. It is a time for individuals to assert their human nature—to listen, to learn, to think, to shout, to be heard.

The strangest aspect of our perilous time is the ominous quiet. Probably never in history has the human race looked so much like sheep marching silently to slaughter. The number of Americans taking any real interest in the arms race or world affairs is pitifully small. In the marketplace and on the golf links, on Madison Avenue and on Main Street, in the factories and on the campuses, the mood is unconcern or resignation. One shrugs one's shoulders—"It can't happen," or "What can one individual do?"

The power of the individual is not negligible; it can be greater, indeed, than 30,000 megatons. Three centuries ago William Bradford, the Governor of the Plymouth Colony, wrote in his *History of Plymouth Plantation:* ". . . as one small candle may light a thousand, so the light here kindled hath shone unto many, yea in some sort to our whole nation." Each citizen in our democracy holds a candle. Let it light a thousand, and the light so kindled will shine in some sort to the whole world.

# *Notes and References*

CHAPTER I

PAGE 5     *BMEWS, SAC,* and *CD*    These symbols stand respectively for Ballistic Missile Early Warning System, Strategic Air Command, and Civil Defense.

6     *its three-megaton missiles*    The 1961 Polaris missile had a power of six-tenths of a megaton. Experts believe that a higher-thrust submarine missile can be developed to carry three megatons.

155

PAGE 6    *emergency base of command*   According to published plans, if a nuclear attack occurred while the President was in Washington, he would be flown to the underground Pentagon near the Pennsylvania border or to a shelter such as that of the Atomic Energy Commission headquarters near Germantown, Maryland.

7    *President Kennedy, explaining his decision to resume nuclear tests*   The quotation is from his radio-television address the evening of March 2, 1962.

7    *General Douglas MacArthur*   From an address by the General on his memorial visit to the Philippine Islands in 1961.

8    *James R. Newman*   This quotation from Mr. Newman, author of *The World of Mathematics* and a member of the board of editors of *Scientific American,* is from a letter to the *Washington Post and Times-Herald.*

8    *W. H. Pickering*   From an article by Dr. Pickering in the *New York Herald Tribune* of January 22, 1958.

10    *President Dwight D. Eisenhower, addressing the United Nations*   This was his famous "Atoms for Peace" speech to the UN on December 8, 1953. The address is available in printed form as Department of State Publication 5403 in its General Foreign Policy Series 88.

PAGE II     *Eugene Rabinowitch*   The quotation is from Dr. Rabinowitch's introduction to a collection of articles published by the *Bulletin of the Atomic Scientists* under the title "Minutes to Midnight" in May 1950.

II     *In weapons research and development . . . the United States spent $80 billion*   This figure is taken from a 1962 publication of the National Science Foundation titled "Trends in Funds and Personnel for Research and Development."

## CHAPTER 2

PAGE 16     *In Bernard Shaw's Man and Superman*   The full quotation of this passage runs: "Have you walked up and down upon the earth lately? I have; and I have examined man's wonderful inventions. And I tell you that in the arts of life man invents nothing, but in the arts of death he outdoes Nature herself, and produces by chemistry and machinery all the slaughter of plague, pestilence, and famine. The peasant I tempt today eats and drinks what was eaten and drunk by peasants 10,000 years ago; and the house he lives in has not altered as much in a thousand centuries as the fashion of a lady's bonnet in a score of weeks. But when he goes out to slay, he carries a marvel of mechanism that lets loose at the touch of his finger all the hidden molecular energies, and leaves the javelin, the arrow, the blowpipe of his fathers far behind."

PAGE 18 *Hans Bethe* This quotation is from an interview of Professor Bethe published by the Center for the Study of Democratic Institutions, Santa Barbara, California, in March 1962. Dr. Bethe remarked: "One major problem which one faces as a scientist lies in the difference in approach to the problem-solving process between scientists and non-scientists. For instance, when one testifies before a Congressional committee, one often has the impression that the purpose of the hearing is not to search out the facts and then reason a solution, but that the solution has been determined, and the hearing will now put such facts on the record as will support the solution. One might say they are not gathering facts but arguments for their position."

19 *scientific advisers, as the President and his Executive departments have done* The President has a Special Assistant for Science and Technology and a Science Advisory Committee. The State Department also has an Office of Science Adviser. The Defense Department has many science advisory committees.

20 *partly responsible for Oppenheimer's later expulsion* Among other reasons for his falling out of favor with the military establish-

ment was his participation in a report called Project Vista, which displeased the Air Force. In this project, undertaken at Caltech in 1951-52 for the Defense Department, Dr. Oppenheimer wrote some recommendations which ran counter to the Air Force doctrine on strategic bombing. The Vista report has never been declassified, but references to it appear in the Oppenheimer hearings.

PAGE 20 *The hearings in the Oppenheimer case* The record of these hearings is available from the United States Government Printing Office under the title: "In the Matter of J. Robert Oppenheimer, Transcript of Hearings before Personnel Security Board." These hearings, held in the period April 12 to May 6, 1954, produced about a million words of testimony.

20 *Dr. Teller's view that the scientist's only job* This quotation is from an article by Dr. Teller, titled "Back to the Laboratories," which was published in the *Bulletin of the Atomic Scientists* in 1950. Paradoxically, Professor Teller has not followed his own advice that scientists should stick to their laboratories, for he has been one of the most vocal scientists on non-scientific issues, such as the question whether the hydrogen bomb should be built.

21 *John von Neumann* He expounded this view in an article in the June 1955 issue of *Fortune,* titled "Can We Survive Technology?"

22 *Harrison Brown* The quotation is from Pro-

fessor Brown's study, "Community of Fear," published in September 1960 by the Center for the Study of Democratic Institutions.

CHAPTER 3

PAGE 23 *a newspaper article in the fall of 1946* This article, discussing the effects of a 50-kiloton bomb, appeared in the *Buffalo Evening News* on November 16, 1946.

28 *practicable size of a fission bomb* Various authorities have estimated that up to one megaton of energy could be obtained from a bomb made solely of fissionable material. The yield from a given amount of such material can be increased, however, by adding fusion material, which supplies neutrons that will fission more of the fissionable core. Thus an A-bomb which would yield half a megaton alone can be made to yield a megaton and a half of fission energy if it is used as the trigger for a thermonuclear bomb.

30 *the shock of the Soviet A-bomb* The U.S.S.R. produced its first atomic bomb two or three years sooner than United States intelligence circles had forecast. The first successful Soviet nuclear explosion, called "Joe I," was detected by a long-range United States monitoring system code-named Operation Vermont.

PAGE 31    *as Bethe said in retrospect*   The quotation is from the Bethe interview published by the Center for the Study of Democratic Institutions (see note on Chapter 2).

32    *"a brilliant discovery . . ."*   This is from Dr. Bethe's testimony in the Oppenheimer hearings (page 330 of the transcript).

34    *The Mike shot amounted to some twelve megatons*   Its yield was estimated at the time to be five megatons, but the first measurements were very rough, and later comparisons with the effects of H-bomb shots raised the estimate of the Mike explosion to twelve megatons.

36    *The moratorium on testing*   A number of United States politicians maintained that the Soviet Union continued to test nuclear weapons underground after 1958. Dr. Teller, in his book *The Legacy of Hiroshima*, declared in 1962 that "the Soviet Union never did stop nuclear tests but was conducting experiments all along." But Dr. Bethe, who was in charge of the panel of experts reviewing intelligence reports during this period, said in 1962 (at a Cornell University lecture on January 5): "As far as I know there has not been any evidence, despite claims to the contrary, that the Russians in fact cheated during the moratorium. . . ."

36    *Premier Nikita Khrushchev announced*

Quoted in the *New York Times* September 8, 1961.

PAGE 36    *58 megatons*    This value for the Soviet explosion was given by President Kennedy in a speech March 2, 1962.

37    *the cost per megaton of a nuclear bomb* The data on costs are taken from a report of the Joint Committee on Atomic Energy, titled "Background Material for the Review of the International Atomic Policies and Programs of the United States," which was published in October 1960.

38    *General Curtis E. LeMay*    Quoted from a speech before the Air Force Association in Philadelphia on September 21, 1961.

38    *Paul H. Nitze*    Speech before the Association of the United States Army in Washington September 7, 1961.

CHAPTER 4

PAGE 40    *Harry S. Truman has written*    Memoirs, by Harry S. Truman, Volume 2, page 302, Doubleday & Company, 1958.

40    *a comment by the late Senator Brien McMahon* From his article, "Should We Reveal the Size of Our Atomic Stockpile?" in the *Bulletin of the Atomic Scientists*, Volume V, page 66 (1949).

PAGE 41 *estimating the amount of their production* I discussed these estimating methods in an article in the *Bulletin* titled "Nuclear Weapon Systems," Volume XVII, page 99 (1961).

43 *the three centers turning out U-235* In the United States fissionable stockpile the amount of U-235 far outweighs that of plutonium, because U-235 is less costly and easier to produce in large quantity.

44 *Early in 1960 John F. Kennedy* Mr. Kennedy, then a United States Senator, gave this estimate of the nuclear stockpile in a speech at the University of New Hampshire on March 7, 1960.

45 *Representative Henry Jackson* The quotations are taken from the *Congressional Record* for October 6, 1951, pages 13129-36.

46 *still rolling on with undiminished vigor* The United States procurement schedules for uranium are projected through 1966, so that the present program apparently calls for full production at least until then.

CHAPTER 5

PAGE 49 *In round numbers some 350 nuclear explosions* During the tests of 1961 and 1962 the Soviet Union and the United States detonated a far greater weight of nuclear bombs than the total of all the tests prior to 1958.

PAGE 50 *The Effects of Nuclear Weapons* The 1962 publication was the third edition of this work; less comprehensive versions were issued in 1950 and 1957. It is a highly technical treatise, presenting much of its information in graphs or mathematical form. The publication is available from the Government Printing Office, Washington, D.C.

50 *the blast effects* The data an these effects are taken from *The Effects of Nuclear Weapons* and from an AEC release, D-279 Rev., dated October 31, 1961. My estimates of the effects of 100-megaton bursts are extrapolations from the information given there on 20-megaton explosions.

52 *The firestorm phenomenon* The data on firestorm effects here are taken from testimony given by Dr. Walmer Strope at hearings on civil defense by the Holifield committee on February 20, 1962. His testimony appears on pages 81-86 of "Civil Defense—1962; Part I, Hearings of the House Committee on Government Operations."

52 *Gerard Piel* From his speech, "The Illusion of Civil Defense," delivered before the Commonwealth Club of San Francisco on November 10, 1961.

53 *the primary flash of this radiation* The nuclear radiation from a one-megaton bomb,

one minute after detonation, is equal to that of ten million tons of radium.

54 *To understand the effects of such radiation* For a detailed discussion of this subject see *Radiation: What It Is and How It Affects You,* by J. Schubert and R. E. Lapp, Viking Press, 1956.

55 *the levels of fallout generated by the nuclear bombs since 1945* See *Fallout,* edited by John M. Fowler, Basic Books, Inc., 1960.

56 *a Navy report inadvertently released in 1953* The report, titled "Radiological Recovery of Fixed Military Installations," was printed in August 1953 as "Restricted Security Information," but it became "unclassified" later that year when the "restricted" category of classification was eliminated.

56 *Brigadier General James Cooney* His statement was made in a joint release of the Defense Department and the AEC, No. 376, on June 13, 1951.

57 *Six years later an obscure, tardily issued report* This report on the *Mike* and *King* shots, bearing the symbols WT-634, UCRL-5125, and AECD-3446, was issued October 17, 1958 but did not become publicly available until July 2, 1959.

58 *The report of this conference was not made public until 1958* The document bore the title "Worldwide Effects of Atomic Weapons

—Project Sunshine," and the symbols AECU-3488, Health and Safety. It was dated August 6, 1953 and was issued under the name of the RAND Corporation. The document was declassified on May 25, 1957, but it was not introduced at the Holified hearings on fallout in that year and was not available to the public until early in 1958. For a discussion of the report see my article, "Sunshine and Darkness," in the *Bulletin of the Atomic Scientists*, Volume XV, page 27 (1959).

PAGE 60    *AEC measurements on certain islands*   The measurements were made at 25 stations in the vicinity. Those to the north of the explosion site recorded no fallout, because of the wind shift. My estimate that lethal fallout missed the *Lucky Dragon* by only ten miles is based on the ship's navigational log and the AEC fallout patterns disclosed in its 1962 *Effects* report.

61    *The full story of this ominous episode*   See my book, *The Voyage of the Lucky Dragon*, Harper & Bros., 1958.

61    *The heavy fallout and the presence of traces of U-237 in the fallout led me to the conclusion*   The Japanese analyses were supplied to me by Professor Charles Coryell of M.I.T. and by some of the Japanese scientists. From the amount of radioactive contamination of the boat and estimated doses received by the fishermen, I deduced that the output of the fission products from the bomb must have

been at least an order of magnitude greater than could be accounted for merely by an A-bomb trigger. As for the fissioning of U-238, it was known that ordinary uranium cannot be fissioned by the comparatively slow neutrons released by the splitting of U-235, but it could be fissioned by the 14-Mev neutrons produced by a thermonuclear reaction. This is known as "fast fission." The U-238 jacket for the fission-fusion-fission bomb could be made of "waste" uranium—that is, the uranium left after U-235 is separated from it in the gaseous diffusion plants.

PAGE 62    *Not until nearly a year afterward did it disclose*   This report of the AEC, called "The Effects of High-Yield Nuclear Explosions," was released February 15, 1955.

63    *The contamination of milk by iodine 131* There is little doubt that this contamination has at times reached dangerous levels in some "hot spots" in the United States as the result of some of the tests. For example, after a bomb test in Nevada on April 25, 1953, the radio-iodine fallout in Troy, New York, was so high that, according to my calculations, the dose received by infants from milk may have been as much as 30 rads.

CHAPTER 6

PAGE 66    *the V-2*   Germany produced some 4,000 V-2s during World War II. Some of these were transported to the United States after the war and used by the Army for rocket experiments.

67    *The United States military planners concluded that the IBM . . . was too great a gamble*   See, for example, Vannevar Bush's book, *Modern Arms and Free Men.*

70    *the Atlas was hitting within two miles of its target*   President Eisenhower, in his State of the Union message to the Congress in 1960, said: "In 14 recent test launchings, at ranges of over 5,000 miles, Atlas has been striking on an average within two miles of the target."

70    *hurled a total weight of some four tons into space*   The weights of the Soviet rockets are taken from data sheets of our National Aeronautics and Space Administration. The estimate of the four-ton rockets' thrust (800,000 pounds) is my own.

72    *vulnerability of the missile bases*   For further details on the hardening of bases and missile strategy see my testimony in the Holifield subcommittee hearings on civil defense, March 30, 1960 (pages 208-255) and my article in the *Bulletin of the Atomic Scientists*

for March 1961 (pages 99-102); also "Deterrent Policies and Missile Systems," a policy statement by the Democratic Advisory Council's Committee on Science and Technology in August 1960; and "Some Calculations on Counterforce Strategies in a General Nuclear War," a study published by the Mershon National Security Program at Ohio State University in August 1959.

PAGE 73    *if the CEP is one mile*    The limit of accuracy possible with an inertial guidance system probably will be about a half-mile.

73    *James E. McDonald*    Dr. McDonald carried on a public campaign to attempt to persuade the Air Force to move the missile sites to downwind locations. His analysis of the fallout hazards was published in the *Journal of the Arizona Academy of Science* of August 1961.

73    *Air Force refused to change the location*    In September 1961, after the sites of these bases had already been fixed, the Defense Department adopted a "Protection Construction Review Guide," but this directive to try to avoid hazards to the population would apply only to future selections of bases.

74    *mounted on moving bases at sea*    Launching of the Polaris from surface ships would have been easier than from submarines, but the submarine was chosen because of its advantage of concealment and the use of nu-

clear engines which could drive a submarine at high speed for great distances under water.

PAGE 76 *The Minuteman* Originally it was planned to place Minutemen on trains which would keep moving about the country (as the Polaris submarine can keep moving), but this plan was abandoned in favor of putting them all in silos. The reasons have not been announced. Testimony given by Lieutenant General James Ferguson at hearings of the House Appropriations Committee on the defense budget for fiscal 1963 indicates that the Air Force opposed cancellation of the train-based program.

76 *readied for firing from its silo within 30 seconds* The authority for this is a statement by General Thomas S. Power which appears on page 7841 of the *Congressional Record* for May 16, 1962.

77 *our U-2 overflights destroyed that security* Details of the U-2 operation and the data obtained from the overflights were published in the *Congressional Record* for April 17, 1962, page 6316. See also the hearings on the U-2 affair by the Senate Foreign Relations Committee, page 124. Also the book *The U-2 Affair*, by D. Wise and T. B. Ross, Random House, 1962.

## CHAPTER 7

PAGE 80    *Secretary of State John Foster Dulles* His speech was made before the Council on Foreign Relations January 12, 1954, and was distributed as a press release by the Department of State.

81    *"The question of the circumstances . . ."* The quotation is from the *New York Times* of March 17, 1954.

83    *the U-2 for high-altitude reconnaissance* Information on the chronology of the U-2 development, and the results of the flights, can be found in the *Congressional Record* for June 7, 1960 (pages 11118-20); July 2, 1960 (pages 14539-46); January 17, 1961 (pages 856-9); and April 17, 1962 (page 6316).

83    *Defense Secretary Thomas S. Gates, Jr.* Quoted from the *Congressional Record* for April 17, 1962.

84    *Nuclear Weapons and Foreign Policy* Dr. Kissinger's book was published by Harper & Bros. for the Council on Foreign Relations in 1957. It contains a foreword by Gordon Dean.

85    *Secretary Dulles embraced it* The Dulles quotation is from his article in *Foreign Affairs* in the fall of 1957.

PAGE 85    *Professor Edward Teller*   His discussion of "humane" nuclear war appeared in an article in *Foreign Affairs* in January 1958.

85    *President Eisenhower*   His statement was made in a press conference on June 26, 1957.

86    *Dr. Kissinger reconsidered*   His article appears in the book *Arms Control, Disarmament and National Security,* edited by D. G. Brennan and published by George Braziller in 1961.

87    *Secretary of Defense Robert S. McNamara*   This important and much-quoted address was made at the commencement exercises of the University of Michigan in Ann Arbor on June 16, 1962.

88    *Soviet Defense Minister Rodion Malinovsky*   His comment appeared in an article in *Pravda* on June 22, 1962.

88    *Air Force spokesmen have maintained*   The Air Force view has been that nuclear bombing of cities is a "diluted deterrent"; this phrase was used by Undersecretary of the Air Force M. A. MacIntyre in a speech on February 4, 1959.

88    *General Thomas S. Power*   Quoted from page 7840 of the *Congressional Record* for May 16, 1962.

88    *Lieutenant General James E. Briggs*   The quotation is from page 2252 of the *Congressional Record* for February 19, 1962. Gen-

eral Briggs originally included this passage in a speech he gave on February 18, 1961, but it was censored from the speech as delivered.

PAGE 89    *Secretary McNamara explained the program to Congress*    The facts and quotations in the following paragraphs are from Mr. McNamara's testimony at the Congressional "Hearings on Military Posture and H.R. 9751" held on January 24, 1962.

89    *National Strategic Target List*    See the House Appropriations Committee Hearings on the Department of Defense appropriations for 1963, Part 3, page 621.

91    *the "mix" of Minuteman and Polaris missiles*    For Secretary McNamara's answer to this question, see the House Appropriations Committee Hearings on the defense appropriations, Part 2, page 24.

CHAPTER 8

PAGE 94    *the RAND Corporation*    According to data submitted to the House Appropriations Committee in connection with the defense budget for 1963, the RAND Corporation had a total of 1,142 employees, of whom 520 were executive, administrative, professional, scientific, and technical. Of these, 239 received salaries above $15,000.

PAGE 94    *Operations research, developed during World War II*   See *Science at War,* by J. G. Crowther and R. Whiddington, Philosophical Library, 1948.

94    *Game theory*   See *Theory of Games and Economic Behavior,* by John von Neumann and Oskar Morgenstern, Princeton University Press, 1944.

96    *NUDETS*   For further information on this system, see the House Committee on Government Operations hearings on "Civil Defense —1962," Part I, page 187, and the House Appropriations Committee hearings on the defense budget for 1963, Part 4, pages 467 and 474-8. The Defense Department assigned responsibility for the system to the Defense Atomic Support Agency, which maintains a Damage Assessment Center with 110 workers and has a $2.5 million contract for technical work with the Stanford Research Institute.

96    *National Resources Evaluation Center*   This center is operated by the Office of Emergency Planning. See the Government Operations Committee hearings on "Civil Defense— 1962," Part I, page 186.

97    *"The Distribution and Effects of Fallout in Large Nuclear-Weapon Campaigns"*   This study was made by Hugh Everett, III, and George E. Pugh of the Institute for Defense Analysis. It was published in *Operations Research,* Volume 7, No. 2 (1959). The authors

stated that it was an independent study "not intended to represent official thinking or plans," but despite this disclaimer the paper is considered authoritative.

PAGE 97 *information from the RAND Corporation* See "Radioactive Contamination from a Multibomb Campaign," by S. M. Greenfield, RAND Memo RM-1969, January 1956.

99 *an attack of only 500 megatons (50 ten-megaton bombs)* The authors assumed that high-yield thermonuclear warheads, deriving two-thirds of their energy from fission, would be used. The use of smaller weapons (*i.e.,* under one megaton) probably would produce a greater overall kill per megaton, because more people would be killed by blast and heat. However, the authors were considering only fallout casualties.

100 *How much study our Government has given to the recovery problem* It appears that there has been very little planning in this area, according to testimony given by officials of the Defense Department and the AEC at the Joint Committee hearings on "Biological and Environmental Effects of Nuclear War." Some of the problems of recovery are outlined in a RAND Corporation "Report on a Study of Non-Military Defense" dated July 1, 1958.

101 *Dr. Herman Kahn* See House Committee on Government Operations hearings on "Civil

Defense—1961," page 171. Dr. Kahn did not present the data on which he based his estimates.

PAGE 102     *Walter Lippmann*     The quotation is from a speech by Mr. Lippmann before the Women's National Press Club in Washington in January 1962.

102     *H. Bentley Glass*     Quoted in the *New York Times* of June 17, 1962.

104     *In an article in the Saturday Evening Post* Mr. Alsop's article, based on an interview with the President, contained the following paragraph:

"Kennedy inherited two basic doctrines on nuclear warfare. One, as we have seen, was that any war bigger than a brushfire war would be a nuclear war from the outset. The other was that the United States would never strike first with the nuclear weapon. Under the Kennedy grand strategy, both doctrines have been quietly discarded."

Immediately after the article appeared, the White House called a special press conference, attended by some 700 newsmen and women. According to the *New York Times* account (March 28, 1962), the White House spokesman who conducted the conference acknowledged that Mr. Alsop had interviewed the President but denied that Mr. Kennedy had "discarded" the United States policies on nuclear warfare.

PAGE 106   *statement in a House of Representatives report*   See page 8, House Report No. 1561 on the Department of Defense Appropriations Bill, April 29, 1960.

106   *George F. Kennan*   His tesimony, here quoted, was given on May 26, 1960, at an executive session of the Committee on Government Operations' Subcommittee on National Policy Machinery, Senator Henry M. Jackson, chairman. It appears on page 848 of Volume 1 of the Subcommittee's hearings on "Organizing for National Security."

108   *Richard B. Russell*   The quotation is from his speech of April 11, 1962, introducing authorization for the Armed Services appropriations. See *Congressional Record,* page 5807.

CHAPTER 9

PAGE 110   *John von Neumann*   Quotation from his *Fortune* magazine article, "Can We Survive Technology?" in June 1955.

111   *General Trudeau spoke of the game*   Quoted from a speech before the Association of the United States Army in Washington September 8, 1961.

111   *As Dr. Bethe has pointed out*   Quotation from a speech January 5, 1962. It was pub-

lished in the *Congressional Record* for February 26, 1962, page A1398.

PAGE 113　　*soft X-rays*　These rays are of longer wavelength than the X-rays used in medical practice and have little penetrating power. They produce heat on being absorbed by the surface of a solid. Their effect might be countered by providing the warhead with a laminated shield.

113　　*a Zeus might score an X-ray kill*　The one-mile range for such a kill is calculated on the basis of a one-megaton explosion, burning off 50 per cent of the attacking missile's heat shield.

116　　*some areas would be dangerous for months* For further details on the hazard of persistent radioactivity see my article, "Fallout and Home Defense," in the May 1959 issue of the *Bulletin of the Atomic Scientists*. If the fallout from 6,000 megatons of fission energy were distributed uniformly over the three million square miles of the United States (assuming two-thirds of the radioactive debris fell within its borders), the radiation one hour after the explosions would be at the rate of 3,000 roentgens per hour—six times the lethal dose. Of course, most of the debris would not come down within an hour. But 12 hours after detonation the debris would still be radiating at the rate of 150 roentgens per hour, and a week afterward the radiation would be 6.5 roentgens per hour, or about 150 roentgens per day. This would be the average over the whole country. In actuality the fallout would not be distributed uniformly, and some areas would be much hotter than others—perhaps ten times hotter than the average.

There is a widespread impression that a nuclear war would coat most of the world with dangerous radioactivity. This is not really the case, for on a global scale the debris would be rather thinly dispersed. The countries directly attacked would, of course, suffer severely from the fallout; elsewhere the effects would be a great deal milder, and long-range rather than immediate.

PAGE 117     *General Curtis E. LeMay*    The quotations are from his address at Assumption College on March 28, 1962.

117     *The issue of shelters*    For a critique of United States civil defense policies and attitudes see *The Shelter-Centered Society,* by Arthur I. Waskow, a report of the Peace Research Institute of Washington, D.C., published January 14, 1962. In this report a group of social and political scientists consider the question: "Will civil defense affect attitudes toward democracy?" They argue that democracy might be seriously endangered by failures, mistakes, or corruption in civil defense.

118     *The first serious effort to launch a shelter program*    See President Kennedy's address

to Congress May 25, 1961—"Urgent National Needs," House Document 174, Eighty-seventh Congress.

PAGE 118    *assigned responsibility for civil defense to the Defense Department*   Originally under the Pentagon, civil defense had been reassigned at various times to the National Security Resources Board, the Federal Civil Defense Administration, and the Office of Civil and Defense Mobilization. The President's Executive Order No. 10052 on July 20, 1961, gave much of the responsibility for civil defense to the Defense Department but left some authority in the Office of Emergency Planning under OCDM.

119    *a program estimated to cost some $6 billion*   See testimony by Assistant Secretary of Defense Steuart L. Pittman at Holifield hearings on "Civil Defense—1962," page 31.

119    *Deputy Secretary of Defense Roswell L. Gilpatric*   The quotations are from a speech given before the United States Civil Defense Council in Washington March 12, 1962.

121    *General Lyman L. Lemnitzer*   See the General's statement, "The Relationship of Civil Defense and Military Strength," at the Holifield hearings on "Civil Defense—1961," page 14.

CHAPTER 10

PAGE 124    *As explained by General Thomas S. Power*
            See his testimony at the House Appropria-
            tions Committee hearings on the Department
            of Defense bill for 1960, Part 2, pages 378-9.

124    *"The Pilot Lights of the Apocalypse"*  The
       playlet was first published in the January
       1946 issue of *Fortune* magazine.

126    *Secretary of State Dean Rusk*  His speech
       was to the New Hampshire Council on World
       Affairs in Concord. See the *New York Times,*
       June 17, 1962.

126    *The possibility of nuclear war "by acci-
       dent. . . ."* Several studies of this subject
       have been published. See "Accidental War:
       Some Dangers in the 1960s," a study by the
       Mershon National Security Program group at
       Ohio State University headed by John Phelps,
       which was published in the *Congressional
       Record* for August 12, 1960, pages 15080-86.
       Also Charles O. Porter's article, "Accident or
       Aggression," in the *Nation* March 5, 1960,
       and Mr. Porter's correspondence with the
       Defense Department published in the *Con-
       gressional Record* for March 31, 1960, pages
       6576-80. Also "Defense, Disarmament and
       Survival," a statement by the Science and

Technology Committee of the Democratic Advisory Council in December 1959, copies of which can be obtained from Counsellors on National Problems, 1028 Connecticut Avenue, N.W., Washington 6, D.C.

PAGE 127    *nuclear weapons have been involved in about a dozen major incidents*   See the Mershon study, "Accidental War," cited above.

128    *special study ordered by President Kennedy* The committee of experts was known as the Fletcher Committee. See testimony of Air Force Secretary Gene Zuckert at the House Appropriations Committee hearings on the Defense Department bill for fiscal 1963, Part 2, pages 530-1.

128    *Lloyd V. Berkner* In his *Foreign Affairs* article Dr. Berkner concluded that "the instability of the armaments situation can only grow worse if present technological trends continue and no political controls are devised."

129    *Charles E. Osgood* Quoted from *Conflict Resolution*, Volume III, page 301 (1959).

129    *one safeguard they recommended* See the *New York Times*, July 6, 1962.

130    *The place had been struck by an asteroid* See the article titled "The Great Meteor of 1947," by Otto Struve, in *Scientific American*, June 1950.

131    *General Power* See his testimony at the House Appropriations Committee hearings

on the Defense Department bill for 1962, Part 2, pages 378-9.

PAGE 132    *Admiral Arleigh Burke*   See the hearings on the Defense Department appropriation for 1962, Part 3, page 339.

132    *McGeorge Bundy*   The quotation is from a speech by Mr. Bundy, titled "The Dangers We Face," before the American Management Association in New York City on January 31, 1962.

135    *General Lauris Norstad*   See General Norstad's testimony before the House Appropriations Committee on June 8, 1959.

136    *C. P. Snow*   Quoted from Sir Charles' address to the American Association for the Advancement of Science at its annual meeting in New York City in December 1960.

## CHAPTER 11

PAGE 137    *Professor A. J. Dempster*   Dr. Dempster, a Canadian-born physicist, pioneered in the science of mass spectroscopy—the technique of separating and studying isotopes of an element by deflecting ions in a magnetic field, which separates them through their difference in weight.

138    *Bulletin of the Atomic Scientists*   Originally called the *Bulletin of the Atomic Scientists of Chicago*, this publication was fathered by

a group in the Metallurgical Laboratory. The *Bulletin* and a closely affiliated organization, the Federation of Atomic Scientists, played an active role in the defeat of the May-Johnson bill and the creation of the Atomic Energy Commission.

PAGE 139    *as Secretary of State Rusk has said*  The quotation is from his speech of June 16, 1962, at Concord, New Hampshire.

139    *The British physicist P. M. S. Blackett*  His article, "Steps toward Disarmament," was published in the April 1962 issue of *Scientific American.*

141    *declared Mr. Khrushchev*  The quotation is from a speech at a Kremlin reception for military academy graduates on July 5, 1962. See the *New York Times*, July 6, 1962.

142    *President Eisenhower repeated the appeal*  See his State of the Union message to Congress on January 9, 1958.

142    *Senator John F. Kennedy*  Quoted from a speech on disarmament December 11, 1959.

144    *Machiavelli cynically observed*  Quotation from *The Prince.*

145    *A workable system of control*  The missile experts R. Roberts and F. McClure have suggested, in a privately circulated proposal titled "A Search for an Alternative to the Arms Race," that submarine-based deterrent forces might be kept by agreement at distances out of range of the potential enemy,

thus reducing the danger of a surprise attack. For example, the United States force might be confined to the Caribbean area and the Soviet force to the Sea of Okhotsk. Any unauthorized move out of these reservations would give warning of a possible attack.

PAGE 146     *Secretary of State Rusk has estimated* In his June 16, 1962 speech the Secretary said that if the arms race continued, the nuclear destructive power could "by 1966 be double what it is today." *New York Times*, June 17, 1962.

146     *Responsibility for our experiments in space is now divided between NASA and the Air Force* The Air Force has charge of more than 90 per cent of all space activities in the Defense Department. According to an article by John W. Finney, a Washington correspondent of the *New York Times*, in the *Times* of June 17, 1962, the Kennedy Administration has given the Defense Department "a freer rein in developing military uses of space . . . in the future there will be increasing emphasis and activities on the military side of the national space program." The test firings of nuclear weapons into space during 1962 tend to confirm this report.

146     *duplication of effort and waste of funds* The United States bill for space activities is now some $5 billion per year. An increase in the duplication of efforts between NASA and the Air Force appears to be in the offing.

PAGE 146  *without secrecy restrictions*  Some of the
military space projects are so highly classified that their names are not even mentioned
in budget requests (*e.g.,* the SAMOS project).

146  *An international communications system*
This should include not only direct, ready
communication between the heads of government (*e.g.,* the White House and the Kremlin) but also information centers on neutral
territory. One of the values of such a system
would be to reduce the danger of precipita-
tion of a general war by a smaller power's
provocative ("catalytic") action for which the
major powers were not responsible.

149  *in his farewell address*  See the text of President Eisenhower's farewell address to the
nation in the *Congressional Record* for February 16, 1961, pages 2094-5.

151  *the Arms Control and Disarmament Agency*
This agency grew out of a proposal made in
1959 by a group at the California Institute of
Technology. The group, a Pasadena subcommittee of the Democratic Advisory Council's
Science and Technology Committee, proposed that the Government establish a
national peace agency "to deal with problems
related to achieving peace through arms limitation agreements, to developing international control and inspection systems, and to
applying scientific and technical resources to
advancing the living standards of peoples in
the underdeveloped nations of the world."

The proposal was approved by the Democratic Advisory Council, and legislation to establish such an agency was introduced by Senator Hubert Humphrey and later, in modified form, by Senator John F. Kennedy. The modified version setting up the United States Arms Control and Disarmament Agency was enacted by the Congress in 1961 after Mr. Kennedy took office as President.

PAGE 152    *To provide the Congress with guidance on scientific matters*    It should be remembered that $1 out of every $7 collected from United States taxpayers goes into expenditures involving science and technology. Without guidance to help it understand the nature of these expenditures, the Congress is ill-equipped to judge the wisdom of the individual items or to exercise control over waste and corruption.

153    *The writer Walter Millis*    The quotation is from an article by Mr. Millis in the *New York Times Magazine* of August 2, 1959.

154    *marching silently to slaughter*    Concerning the possibility of nuclear war, there is a striking contrast between the attitude of the public and that of the experts who have been close to the problem—that is, Government leaders, military men, scientists, etc. Whereas most people have a general feeling that the vastly destructive nuclear weapons have made a great war extremely unlikely, the experts do not share this belief. Their views

can be summed up in a few representative comments:

John Foster Dulles: "Future generations will look back with amazement if war is averted."

Dean Rusk: "We must eliminate the instruments of destruction."

Thomas K. Finletter, former Secretary of the Air Force: "These modern weapons are simply too hot to handle, and as time goes on the curve of probability that they will go off will steadily rise."

General Thomas Power, commander of SAC: "There would be no use whatever in maintaining our expensive military establishment if we are so convinced of the futility of nuclear war that we are too scared to face it."

Harrison Brown: "If developments continue in the future as they have during the last 15 years, I believe that an all-out nuclear war involving the Soviet Union and the United States is, in the long run, inevitable."

Andrei A. Gromyko, Soviet Foreign Minister: "Every year, every month lost for disarmament is not just marking time . . . but a lightning-fast slide to the red line separating peace from the blast of rocket nuclear war."

History speaks even more grimly on this subject. During the past 500 years civilized man has waged about 300 wars. In the twentieth century the average has been about three wars per decade, and of these, two were world wars.

# Index

A-bomb, 17, 33
  birth of, 23
  critical mass, 25-26
  early rockets for, 67
  first, 26, 55
  high-yield, 28
  as trigger in H-bomb, 33-35
accidental war, 9, 118, 123-136
  prevention of, 146-147
AEC, *see* Atomic Energy Commission
Aerobee rocket, 68
AFOAT-1, 83
aggression, deterrence and, 81-84
AICBM, 110
  bases for, 114
Air Force, U.S., 10, 38, 65, 68-69, 73, 94, 116
  and Atomic Energy Commission, 83-84

rivalry with Navy, 27, 76, 88
Alamogordo, N. M., 26
Alsop, Joseph, 40
Alsop, Stewart, 40, 105
American Bar Association, 46
American cities, destruction of, 73
American Psychological Association, 129
animals, destruction of, 99, 102-103
annihilation, by accident, 123
  strategy of, 8, 10
anticipatory attack, 84
  *see also* first-strike attack
anti-missile missile, 109-110, 114
arms control, 143-144, 150
  need for, 147-148
Arms Control and Disarmament Agency, 150-151

arms industry, 148
arms race, 35, 138, 150-154
  step-up in, 68
  turning point in, 141
Army, U.S., 109
Army Air Defense Command, 109
*Art of Projecting Bombs, The,* 78
asteroid, fall of in Soviet Union, 130-131
Atlas missile, 66, 69-73, 149
atomic bomb, *see* A-bomb
atomic energy:
  civilian vs. military control of, 20, 138
  Joint Committee on, 19, 30, 41, 45-46, 100
Atomic Energy Act (1946), 59, 125
Atomic Energy Commission, 19, 28, 30-34, 40, 45, 49, 56-57, 62, 102, 118, 130, 145
  Air Force and, 83-84
  creation of, 138
  electric bill of, 43
atomic scientists, lobby of, 138
  *see also* science; scientists
atomic submarine, 74-76
  *see also* Polaris missile
attack, hypothetical, 5
  *see also* nuclear attack; nuclear warfare

ballistic missile, first, 66
Ballistic Missile Booster Interception, 116
Ballistic Missile Early Warning System, *see* BMEWS
bazooka missile, 28, 86
Belgian Congo, 24
Berkner, Lloyd V., 128
Berlin crisis, 118
Bethe, Hans, 18, 31-32, 37, 77, 110-111
Bevin, Ernest, 12
B-52 bombers, 69, 126, 139
Bikini tests, 34, 55-59
"Biological and Environmental Effects of Nuclear War," 100
Blackett, P. M. S., 139
blast effects, 49-63
BMEWS (Ballistic Missile Early Warning System), 6, 110

bombers vs. missiles, 65
bomb materials, "mothballing" of, 145-146
bombs, "clean" vs. "dirty," 36-37, 55-56, 61, 85
  delivery systems for, 65
  families of, 38
  megaton, 37, 72
"bonus kills," 100
Bradford, William, 154
*Bravo* shot, H-bomb, 34, 59, 61-62
Briggs, Lt. Gen. James E., 88
Brown, Harrison, 22
budgets, Congress and, 18
Bugher, John C., 62-63
*Bulletin of the Atomic Scientists,* 11, 138
Bundy, McGeorge, 132
Burke, Adm. Arleigh, 132

California, University of, 34
California Institute of Technology, Jet Propulsion Laboratory, 8
Cape Canaveral, 70
"Castle" tests, 34, 69
Castro, Fidel, 106
Central Intelligence Agency, 89
CEP (circular error probability), 67-68, 70, 73
chain reaction, 25
  first, 138
Chicago, University of, 137
Childs, Marquis W., 151
Churchill, Sir Winston S., 79, 92
cities, destruction of, 73, 120, 140
civil defense, need for, 121
Civil Defense Organization, 118
civilization, "hope" of, 137-154
Clausewitz, Karl von, 39, 93
"clean" vs. "dirty" bombs, 36-37, 55-56, 61, 85
Clemenceau, Georges, 11
Cold War, 4, 8, 45, 105
Columbia River, Washington, 43
Columbia University, 29
communications satellite, 146
communications system, international, 146-147

Communist aggression, deterrence policy and, 91-92
Communist China, 6, 81-82, 131, 143-144
    nuclear threat of, 108, 136
computers, in nuclear age, 17, 22, 75, 93-96
Congress, U.S., 12, 18
    guidance for, 152
    military posture of, 149
Congress of Scientists on Survival, 102-103
Congressmen, science and, 18-19
Constitution, U.S., 4
control and inspection systems, 142, 145
Convair Division, General Dynamics Corporation, 68-69
Cooney, Brig. Gen. James, 56
Corporal missile, 86
counter-strike, 103-104
critical mass, 25

Davy Crockett missile, 28, 86
Dean, Gordon, 46-47
death rays, 117
deaths, from nuclear attack, 97-98, 120
defense, active vs. passive, 109, 117-118
    information on, 11
Defense Atomic Support Agency, 94
defense contracts, employment and, 118, 148
Defense Department, U.S., 10, 17-18, 49, 67, 74, 89, 94, 96, 118-119, 148, 150-151
defensive system, U.S., 109-121
Dempster, A. J., 137
deterrent, and Communist aggression, 91-92
    fallout shelters as, 121
    first-strike strategy and, 107
    and "massive retaliation," 80-82
    minimum, 140
    vs. overkill, 145
    paradox of, 79-92
    SAC missions and, 88
    submarine-based, 145
    as strategic concept, 80

deuterium, 29, 32
"dirty" vs. "clean" bombs, 36-37, 55-56, 61, 85
disarmament, 133-134
    vs. civil defense, 122
    as "hope of civilization," 137-154
Dulles, Allen W., 89
Dulles, John Foster, 80-85

education, need for in nuclear age, 153
Effects of Nuclear Weapons, 50, 60
Einstein, Albert, 21
Eisenhower, Dwight D., 10, 80, 84-85, 104, 123, 141, 149
electronics, military, 17, 93, 129
Elugelab Island, 33, 57
Engebi Island, 57
Eniwetok atoll, 27, 33, 57
Europe, recovery of from World War II, 102

fallout, 49-64
    as "bonus kill," 100
    deaths from, 97-98
    from H-bomb tests, 63
    in Lucky Dragon incident, 60-62
    in nuclear war, 73, 96-97
Fallout Protection, 119
fallout shelters, 117-121
Fermi, Enrico, 29
F-F-F bomb, 62
Finletter, Thomas K., 80, 103
fire effects, 49-63
firestorm, 50-52
first-strike attack, 84, 92, 96
    accuracy of, 91
    vs. deterrence, 145
    vs. retaliation, 103-104
fission bomb, 28
    see also H-bomb
fissionable materials, investment in production of, 41-43
fission-fusion-fission bomb, 62
F-104 jet fighter, 83
Foreign Affairs, 128
Formosa, 131
France, nuclear threat of, 107-108

Franck, James, 138

Gaither Report, 105
game theory, nuclear war and, 94
gamma radiation, 53
in anti-missile attack, 113
Gardner, Trevor, 68
Gates, Thomas S., Jr., 83-84
Gaulle, Charles de, 107
G-bomb, 38, 115
Geiger counters, 59-60
General Dynamics Corporation, 68, 149
genetic damage, 99
German rocket experts, 67
German submarines, World War II, 94
gigaton bomb, 38, 115
Gilpatric, Roswell L., 119
Glass, H. Bentley, 102
graphite reactor, 42
Griffiss Air Force Base, 148

Hanford reactor, Washington, 42, 145
"hard" missile bases, 72
H-bomb, 6, 10, 41, 43
blast, fire and fallout effects of, 49-63
cost per ton of explosive power, 37
deaths per megaton, 97-99
development of, 29
first explosion of, 33, 56
jettisoning of by U.S. bomber, 127
largest exploded to date, 36
100-megaton, 72-73
"open-ended," 37
radiation effects of, 63
size of, 37-38
Soviet, 71, 77-78
uranium-238 in, 61-62
Hiroshima bomb, 12, 21, 23, 26, 29, 41, 43, 50, 53, 75, 132, 141
fallout effects, 55
firestorm in, 52
survivors of, 120-121
Hitler, Adolf, 66, 92, 135
Holifield, Chet, 73-74
Humphrey, Hubert, 126

Hunter's Point, San Francisco, 56
hydrazine, 72
hydrogen, fusion of, 29
hydrogen bomb, see H-bomb
hydrogen isotopes, 31-32
hypothetical attack and retaliation, 5-6

IBM (missile), 67
ICBM (intercontinental ballistic missile), 4, 9-10, 21-22, 38, 53, 66, 68, 131, 138, 141
accidental firing of, 127
and anti-ICBM, 110
Atlas launcher for, 71
"decision time" and, 124
gamma-ray interception of, 113
number of U.S., 139
vs. Polaris missile, 75
of Soviet Union, 71, 77, 132-133
see also Atlas missile; Titan missile
Industrial Health Conference, 62
industrial plant, "expendable," 101
industrial reorientation, 150-151
inertial guidance system, 75-76
infrared sensors, 110
intercontinental ballistic missile, see ICBM
International Geophysical Year, 128

Jackson, Henry, 45
jet bombers, long-range, 68
Jet Propulsion Laboratory, California Institute of Technology, 8
Johnson, Byron, 149
Johnson, Edwin C., 30
Joint Chiefs of Staff, 89
Joint Committee on Atomic Energy, 19, 30, 41, 45-46, 100, 129
Joint Target Evaluation Group, 89-90
Joint Task Force, U.S., 59
Jumbo II, 96

Kahn, Herman, 95, 101
Kennan, George F., 106
Kennedy, John F., 3, 7, 12, 44,
    87, 105, 118-119, 123, 128-
    129, 132, 142-143, 150
Khrushchev, Nikita S., 36, 38,
    71, 77, 84, 118, 126, 141
killing, diffused guilt for, 22
kiloton bombs, 37
Kimura, Kenjiro, 61
Kissinger, Henry M., 84-87
Korean War, 45, 81

lead vs. uranium, 24, 36
Legacy of Hiroshima, The, 100
LeMay, Gen. Curtis E., 38, 117
Lemnitzer, Gen. Lyman L., 121
Libby, Willard F., 118
Life magazine, 118
Lippmann, Walter, 102, 105
lithium deuteride, 34
Lockheed Aircraft Corporation,
    83
London, V-2 bombing of, 66
Long John missile, 86
Los Alamos Laboratory, 26-27,
    30-31
Lucky Dragon incident, 34, 60-62

MacArthur, Gen. Douglas, 7-8
McDonald, James E., 73
McElroy, Neil, 105
Machiavelli, Niccolo, 144
MacIntyre, M. A., 105
McMahon, Brien, 40-41, 45
McMahon Atomic Energy Bill,
    138
McNamara, Robert S., 87-91, 107,
    139
madness, attack as result of, 134-
    135
Malinovsky, Rodion, 87
Man and Superman, 16
Manhattan Project, 24-25, 30, 55
Marshall Island, 34
"massive retaliation" policy, 45,
    80-82, 85
mathematical techniques, 93-95
May-Johnson Bill, 138
"megadeaths," 100
megaton bombs, 37, 72-73
meteorite, danger of, 130

Michelsen, Lt. Gen. Stanley R.,
    109
Midas satellites, 110
Mike shot (1952), 32, 34, 56, 58,
    68
military employment, as "natural
    condition," 21-22, 148-149
milk, radiation products in, 63
Millis, Walter, 153
Minuteman missile, 76
    accidental firing of, 127-128
    and Polaris "mix," 91
miscalculation, war through, 123-
    136
missile bases, U.S., 10, 72-74
"missile gap," 140
missile program, revision of as
    retaliatory force, 144
missiles:
    vs. bombers, 65
    number and size of, 65-78
    tactical, 86
    underwater bases for, 145
    see also Atlas; ICBM; Minute-
    man; Polaris; Titan
Morgan, Russell H., 63

Nagasaki bomb, 27, 30, 113
    fallout effects of, 55
NASA (National Aeronautics and
    Space Administration), 146,
    149
National Advisory Committee on
    Radiation, 63
national defense, importance of,
    11
National Resources Evaluation
    Center, 96
National War College, 89
NATO (North Atlantic Treaty
    Organization), 87, 107, 135
Navy, U.S., Special Projects Of-
    fice, 74
    vs. Air Force in nuclear arms
    race, 27, 76, 88
Neumann, John von, 21, 68, 94,
    110
neutron kill, of ICBM warhead,
    113
Newman, James R., 8
Nike-Zeus anti-missile bases, 111-
    115

nitrogen tetroxide, 72
Nitze, Paul H., 38
Norad (North American Air Defense Command), 5-6
Norstad, Gen. Lauris, 135
Novaya Zemlya, U.S.S.R., 36
Novopokrovka, U.S.S.R., 130
*n*th-country problem, 108
nuclear age, birth of, 137
nuclear attack, survival in, 120-121
nuclear detection system (NUDETS), 96
nuclear materials, "mothballing" of, 145-146
nuclear strategy, U.S., 9-10, 87-89
nuclear submarines, 74-76
nuclear tests, moratorium on, 36
nuclear warfare:
    accidental, 9, 118, 123-136
    animal destruction in, 99, 102-103
    "clean" bombs in, 36-37, 61, 85
    "code" of, 84-85
    deaths from, 97-98, 120
    defense possibilities in, 109-121
    fallout in, 73
    "game" of, 93-108
    "limited," 84-87
    as national suicide, 143
    odds favoring outbreak of, 141
    probable damage and casualties in U.S., 96-97
    radiation effects of, 63
    "reconstruction" following, 101-102
    study of effects of, 147
    "winner" in, 96, 100, 142-143, 147
nuclear warheads, 65-66
    destruction of, 112
nuclear weapons:
    accidents with, 127-128
    Army-Navy rivalry over, 27, 76, 88
    blast, fire, and fallout effects of, 49-63
    family of, 23-38
    growth of, 23-24, 37-38
    low-yield, 28

race between U.S. and Soviet Union in, 35, 68, 141, 150-154
    scientists and, 20
    statistics on, 41-42, 139-140
    stockpile of, 10, 39-46
    tactical use of, 86, 134
*Nuclear Weapons and Foreign Policy*, 84-85
NUDETS (nuclear detection system), 96

Oak Ridge, Tenn., plant, 26, 42, 146
Office of Industrial Orientation, 150-151
Operation Buster-Jangle, 28
Operation Castle, 34, 69
Operation Crossroads, 55
Operation Ranger, 28
operations research, U.S., 94
*Operations Research* (pub.), 97
Oppenheimer, J. Robert, 10, 20, 26
Osgood, Charles E., 129
overkill, 10
    vs. deterrence, 145
    vs. slowkill, 62

Paducah, Ky., plant, 42
Parsons, Rear Adm. W. S., 27
peace, rational behavior and, 129
Peenemunde missile base, Germany, 67
Pentagon, *see* Defense Department, U.S.
Pershing missile, 86
physicists, need for, 17
Pickering, W. H., 8-9
Piel, Gerard, 52
*Pilot Lights of the Apocalypse, The*, 124-125
plasma physics, 21
plutonium, 27-29, 42, 58
Polaris missile, 74-76, 88
    and Minuteman "mix," 91
    number of, 139
    submarines and, 134
politics, science and, 18
Portsmouth, Ohio, plant, 42
Power, Gen. Thomas S., 88, 124, 131

President, U.S., in nuclear age, 152-153
ultimate decision by, 4-5
Project Bambi, 116
Project MX-774, 67
Project Sunshine, 58, 63
Project Super, 29
pushbutton war, start of, 135-136

Quesada, Gen. Elwood R., 56

Rabinowitch, Eugene, 11, 138
Raborn, Rear Adm. William F., 74
radar, 17
detection by, 110
radiation effects, 53-57, 63, 97
radioactive cloud, death from, 116
radio-iodine, 63
Radiological Defense Laboratory, 56
radiostrontium, 58, 62-63
radium watch dials, 58
RAND Corporation, 57-58, 94, 97
research and development, in weaponry production, 11-12
retaliation, massive, 45, 80-82, 85
retaliatory force:
deterrence through, 95
pre-aimed, 103-104
missile program as, 144-145
Ridenour, Louis, 124, 130
rocket fuel, 72
rocketry, growth of, 66-67, 70-71
roentgen dosage, 54-57
lethal, 63
Rusk, Dean, 126, 139, 146
Russell, Bertrand, 141
Russell, Richard B., 108
Rutherford, Ernest, 21

SAC (Strategic Air Command), 5, 63-64, 88, 99, 124, 131
fail-safe system of, 124
safety lock, on nuclear warheads, 129, 134
satellites:
bomb-carrying, 90, 116
peaceful, 146
Saturday Evening Post, 104
Saturn missile, 66

Savannah River project, S. C., 32, 43
Schriever, Brig. Gen. Bernard A., 69
science:
politics and, 18
tragedy of, 15-22
weaponry and, 21
Scientific American, 52, 139
scientists:
devotion to weaponry, 21-22
subsidization of, 17-18
second-strike, strategy of, 92, 95, 103
security, quest for, 139
Sergeant missile, 86
Shaw, Bernard, 16
shelter program, U.S., 117-121
SINS (ship's inertial navigation system), 75-76
slowkill vs. overkill, 62
Snow, C. P., 136
solid-fuel rocket, 75
Soviet Union:
A-bomb development by, 27-30
"accidental" attack from, 131-132
arms race with, 68
asteroid impact in, 130-131
breaks moratorium on nuclear tests, 36
"brute-force" rocketry of, 70-71
counter-attack on, 94-95
disarmament talks, 126, 142
first-strike strategy of, 104-106
H-bomb development, 34
ICBMs of, 77
"imaginary war" with, 94
industrial capacity of, 102
largest H-bomb explosion by, 36, 77-78
"minimum deterrent" policy of, 140
missile bases of, 77-78
nuclear strategy of, 88, 139-140
"overkilling" of, 44
possible war with, 94
"preventive" attack on, 105
space agreements with, 146
Sputniks of, 70-71, 132-133
striking force of, 139

Soviet Union (*cont'd*)
  targets in, 83, 89-90
  U-2 reconnaissance flights over, 83-84
  vulnerability to attack, 141
  World War II casualties in, 95
space, as "out of bounds" for military operations, 146
space stations, bomb-carrying, 90, 116
space supremacy, war for, 117
Sprague, Robert, 105
Sputniks, 70-71
  bomb-carrying, 132-133
stockpile, of nuclear weapons, 39-46
  size of, 139-140
Strategic Air Command, *see* SAC
strategic retaliatory force, 89-90
strategy, of annihilation, 8, 10
  U.S. policies of, 9-10, 87-89
Stratton, Samuel S., 148
Strauss, Lewis L., 47, 62, 85
strontium-90, 58
  increase of, 62-63
submarines:
  anti-missile defense with, 115
  as deterrent, 91, 145
  German, 94
  Polaris, *see* Polaris missile
suicide, nuclear war as, 143
superbombs, effects of, 52-53
Symington, Stuart, 140
Szilard, Leo, 138


target-tracking radar, 111
Tartaglia, Niccolo, 78
Teller, Edward, 20, 29, 32-33, 85-86, 95, 100, 118
Telstar communications satellite, 146
terror, peace through, 79
tidal wave, 115-116
Titan missile, 66, 71-73, 149
TNT, atom bomb and, 24-26
Tokyo, University of, 61
tritium, 32
Trudeau, Gen. Arthur G., 109, 111
Truman, Harry S., 30, 141

unemployment, arms control and, 148
United Nations, 3, 10, 80, 104, 123, 147
United States:
  Congress of the, *see* Congress, U.S.
  deaths in nuclear attack, 120
  Defense Department, *see* Defense Department, U.S.
  defense expenditures, 17, 139, 148
  defensive position of, 109-121
  "first-strike" strategy of, 104-106
  fissionable materials production in, 42-43
  missile bases in, 10
  nuclear stockpile of, 39-46
  nuclear strategy of, 87-88
  nuclear superiority over Soviet Union, 139-140
  probable nuclear damage and casualties in, 96-97
  R&D expenditures on weapon production, 11-12
  "recovery" from nuclear attack, 100-101
  rise of atomic stockpile in, 44-46
  strategic policies of, 9-10, 87-89
  vulnerability to radioactive cloud, 116
  *see also* Air Force; Defense Department; Navy, U.S.
universities, defense contracts with, 17
Upshot-Knothole tests, 28
uranium, 58
  atomic bomb and, 24
  vs. lead in H-bomb jacket, 36-37
  vs. tritium, 32
uranium hexafluoride, 42
uranium-235, 25, 42
uranium-237, 61
uranium-238, 35, 42, 61-62
Urey, Harold, 29
U.S.S.R., *see* Soviet Union
U-2 reconnaissance flights, 77, 83, 90, 104

V-2 rockets, World War II, 66
von Neumann Committee, 68-69
  *see also* Neumann, John von

WAC Corporal rocket, 68
War Department, U.S., 23, 67
  *see also* Defense Department, U.S.
warfare, scale of, 10
  *see also* nuclear warfare
weapon production, R&D in, 11-12
weaponry, as permanent element of society, 21-22
weapons:
  invention and development of, 15
  R&D expenditures, U.S., 11-12
  *see also* nuclear weapons
Western Development Division, U.S. Air Force, 69
Western Germany, 143-144

West German Air Force, 129
White, Gen. Thomas D., 74
World War II:
  destruction in, 21
  economic adjustment after, 150
  firestorms in, 51
  new technologies resulting from, 17
  physical recovery from, 102
  security expenditures since, 139
  "Worldwide Effects of Atomic Weapons," 58

xenon, 29
X-rays, 54
  anti-missile, 113

Zeus missile, *see* Nike-Zeus missile